set yourself free

Welcome to Issue 2 of the One Stop Guide to the Isle of Man.

Within this Guide you will find a host of attractions and details of how to get there.

The Guide has colour coded sections to enable you to find the area of your choice quickly and details of all sections can be found in the index on pages 1 & 2.

At the rear of the Guide is a comprehensive list of bus services and their destinations along with detailed route maps.

Emergency Phone Numbers
999 for Fire, Police, Ambulance or Coastguard
Emergency text message number **166999,** this service is restricted to people with hearing or speech impairments.

Other services
Emergency Calls Only; Electric - **687687,** Gas - **644444,**
Water - **695999**
Main Hospital - Noble's Hospital Douglas - **650000**
Mann Doc - **650355**
Emergency Dentist - **650000**
Emergency Information for Divers - **626394**

Department of Tourism and Leisure
Issue 2 May 2009, information correct at time of going to press.

Main Towns/Villages

Douglas (Doolish)

The Island's capital has much to offer the visitor and is undergoing a major renaissance at the present time. The impressive two-mile sweep of Douglas Bay is home to a vibrant town. Its main shopping area behind Loch Promenade at its southern end, boasts many well-known UK High Street stores and a host of independents. Befitting a capital, Douglas has an abundance of good quality hotels, guest-houses and restaurants and the re-generation of the town's inner-harbour has seen the creation of a yacht marina and a pleasant quayside leisure area. The excellent Villa Marina entertainment complex and the stunning Frank Matcham designed Gaiety Theatre, both on the seafront, are just a couple of the jewels in the town's crown. Sports enthusiasts can make use of the fabulous National Sports Centre to the south of the town.

Onchan (Kiondroghad)

Onchan lies just north of Douglas and has a number of unique attractions of its own. Onchan Leisure Park and Stadium offers activities ranging from Stock Car Racing (in season) to a boating lake and bowling greens. Nearby the challenging King Edward Bay Golf Course on Onchan Head affords panoramic views of Douglas Bay to the south and Groudle to the north. In the village centre old meets new. Highlights of the old village include the parish church of St Peter's, built in 1833, which is the site of a former church where Captain Bligh of the Bounty was married. Close by is washerwoman Molly Carroon's Cottage which dates back to the mid 1700s. On the outskirts of the village are two of the Island's national glens – Molly Quirk's Glen and Groudle Glen.

Castletown (Balley Cashtal)

The Island's ancient capital is dominated by Castle Rushen, a magnificently preserved medievel fortress and former home to Kings and Lords of Mann. The castle, which was built between the 13th and 16th centuries, is open to the public between Easter and October and is also a popular location for weddings. It overlooks an idyllic harbour to one side and the town square to the other. Castletown has much offer the visitor. Attractions include the old House of Keys building where the Island's early laws were debated, The Nautical Museum – home to the yacht Peggy which played a major role in the smuggling trade and the Old Grammar School which retains the fixtures and fittings that were in place when it closed for the last time in 1930.

Port St Mary (Purt le Moirrey)

The picturesque coastal village of Port St Mary offers an excellent beach and a pleasing yacht harbour and fishing port. The village is home to the Isle of Man Yacht Club and also provides a great starting point for a series of excellent coastal walks. Port St Mary High Street features a number of welcoming hostelries, a chippy and an award winning restaurant. An excellent nine-hole golf course is another attraction of this popular seaside village..

set yourself free

Port Erin (Purt Chiarn)

Imposing Port Erin sits within a beautiful bay dominated to its northern side by towering Bradda Head. Its beach is one of the Island's finest, offering soft golden sands and the area is a walker's paradise with spectacular glen and coastal pathways. The attractions of Port Erin don't stop at its natural beauty. The town offers a range of good hotels, pubs and eateries along with several independent shops and a supermarket. Port Erin is the southern outpost of the Steam Railway and within the surrounds of the station is the excellent Railway Museum. Boat trips to the Calf of Man depart from Port Erin harbour.

St Johns (Balley Keeill Eoin)

The quiet rural village of St Johns takes centre stage on Manx National Day, July 5th when the annual open air Tynwald ceremony is held. During the proceedings, Acts passed by the Manx parliament in the preceding year are promulgated. Tynwald members gather on the tiered hill on the village green. St Johns has a number of excellent attractions including the lovely arboretum adjacent to Tynwald Hill and Cooill y Ree Gardens, a haven of peace and tranquillity spanning more than three acres. Shopaholics can feed their habit at the lovely Tynwald Mills shopping complex in the valley behind the village. The facilities include two excellent cafes.

Peel (Purt ny hInshey)

Peel has quaint, narrow streets, a deep, working harbour lined with fishing boats and pleasure craft and the magnificent ruins of Peel Castle all combine to create a unique atmosphere. The Castle stands on St Patrick's Isle and dates back to the 11th century. History is given a modem, interactive twist in the nearby House of Manannan. This award-winning museum charts key elements in the Island's history. The Leece Museum is devoted to objects, photographs and documents specifically relating to Peel in the Isle of Man. Peel Centenary Centre is a popular venue for music and dance shows, along with panto, plays, poetery and lectures. Peel has a good selection of shops, cafes, restaurants and traditional public houses – as well as one of the Island's finest sandy beaches. It's also the home of the Island's world famous kipper curing industry and its only cathedral – St German's.

Ramsey (Rhumsaa)

The Island's second largest town earned the title 'Royal Ramsey' after an unscheduled visit in 1847 by Queen Victoria and Prince Albert. Ramsey sits on the northern plain at the foot of the northern mountain range and boasts the highest number of sunshine hours of all the Island's main towns. The town centre offers a good range of mainly independent shops, cafes and public houses. There's an attractive working harbour spanned by a Victorian swing bridge and open expanses of sand/shingle beach to the north and south of the town. Ramsey's jewel is the 40 acre Mooragh Park – a pristine leisure facility with a large boating lake, cafes, bowling green, tennis courts and children's playground – all interspersed with beautifully manicured gardens.

Laxey (Laksaa)

Laxey is set in a beautiful deep valley and forms two distinct areas – the main village and Old Laxey, which nestles around the quaint tidal harbour. The sand/shingle beach at Laxey is extremely popular with visitors and locals alike and the coast between Laxey and Dhoon (to the north) is a popular location for whale watchers in the autumn months. The village is dominated by the magnificent Laxey Wheel. It's the biggest working water wheel in the world and was built in 1854 to pump water from the lead and zinc mines. The Laxey Wheel now has a little sister in the form of the Lady Evelyn – or the Snaefell Wheel. She was dismantled in 1910 but has now been fully restored. At Laxey Woollen Mills, visitors can see the famous Manx tartan being made on original looms.

Become an Island Explorer

Buy a great value Island Explorer ticket and you'll have the freedom to travel when and where you like on scheduled services of the Steam Railway, Manx Electric Railway, Snaefell Mountain Railway, Buses (excluding Manx Express) and the Douglas Corporation horse trams. There are also great savings for children travelling with full fare-paying adults.

For full details call 01624 662525

Visit www.iombusandrail.info or call into the Isle of Man Welcome Centre at the Sea Terminal in Douglas.

Manx National Heritage

5 Site 5 day pass Tickets are available from all 13 Story of Mann attractions, Sea Terminal Welcome Centre and Post Offices throughout the Island.

RAILWAYS

Railways

Isle of Man Steam Railway

Dating from 1874 the Isle of Man Steam Railway is the Island's oldest Victorian rail system. Locomotive No 4, 'Loch' is one of the original engines and is still in service today. The lines once covered 50 miles but now only the southern section survives, running between Douglas and Port Erin, offering stunning countryside and coastal views and calling at Port Soderick, Santon, Ballasalla, Castletown, Ballabeg, Colby, Port St Mary and Port Erin. Journey time is approximately 59 minutes in either direction between Douglas and Port Erin. Steam trains stop by request at Santon, Ronaldsway Halt, Ballabeg and Colby Level. When you board, tell the guard where you wish to alight. To board the train give a clear hand signal to the driver.

During December children and their parents can enjoy the Santa specials

⊕	Route	Between Douglas and Port Erin Stations approx. 59 minutes
🚪	Open	Easter - Oct/Nov
💷	Tariff	Fares charged
🚗	Parking	Ample at main stations
♿	Disabled access	Limited Access on request
☎	Landline	+ 44 (0) 1624 662525
🖱	Website	www.iombusandrail.info

Manx Electric Railway

For some of the finest views of the east coast take a trip on the Manx Electric Railway first opened in 1893, running originally from Douglas to Laxey and extended to Ramsey in 1899. Its 17 miles of track are acknowledged as the longest narrow gauge vintage railway system in the British Isles. All the trams are original, the most recent dating from 1906, the oldest from 1893. In the 1950s the Isle of Man Government purchased the railway and the service now operates with both saloon and open cars from Easter to the end of October.

A visitor centre at the Ramsey MER terminus houses a collection of photographs that tell the story of the railway.

	Route	Douglas to Ramsey via Laxey approx. 75 mins
	Open	Easter - Oct/Nov
	Tariff	Fares charged
	Parking	Ample at main stations
	Disabled access	Limited Access on request
	Landline	+ 44 (0) 1624 662525
	Website	www.iombusandrail.info

Snaefell Mountain Railway

For a spectacular view, on a clear day, of seven kingdoms – Mann, Scotland, England, Wales, Ireland, Heaven and the Sea– take a ride on the only electric mountain railway in the British Isles. Started in 1895, the three and a half feet gauge railway, which took just seven months to complete, runs a total of four miles, climbing out from the village of Laxey up to the Island's highest point, the summit of Snaefell (Snow Mountain), which stands 2036 feet (621 metres) above sea level.

There is a tram stop at the half-way point known as 'The Bungalow' on the Mountain Road (a section of the world famous TT course), convenient for motorists as there is ample car parking space. For the more energetic a path leads from The Bungalow to the summit, where there is a café and ticket station.

Journey time is thirty minutes in each direction. Even in summer the summit can be cold and windy, so dress warmly.

	Route	Laxey - Snaefell approx. 30 mins
	By Bus	3, 3A, 3B, 3C, X3 and MER
	Open	End of April until end of September
	Tariff	Fares charged
	Parking	Ample at main stations
	Disabled access	Limited Access on request
	Landline	+ 44 (0) 1624 662525
	Website	www.iombusandrail.info

Bus services commence from Douglas and Ramsey Bus Stations to all towns and villages. See pages 185 and 186

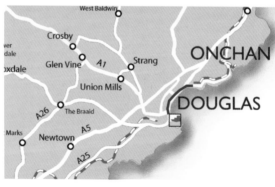

Douglas Horse Trams

Owned and operated by Douglas Corporation these are the world's oldest surviving horse trams, dating from 1876, with many of the original cars still in use. The tramway was designed by Thomas Lightfoot, who was originally from Sheffield but retired to the Isle of Man. The three-feet gauge tramway runs along Douglas promenade from the Manx Electric Railway terminus at Derby Castle to the Sea Terminal and has operated almost continually since its opening, with the exception of World War II. Of the 51 original cars, some 20 are still operational, maintained in-house at the Derby Castle sheds. The fleet includes open and enclosed cars, 'toastracks' and double deckers.

The horses which are purchased by Douglas Corporation as yearlings, begin pulling trams when they are about four years old and have an average working life of 15 years. The horses that pull the tramcars are known as 'trammers' and work no longer than two hours a day. On retirement trammers spend the rest of their life at The Home of Rest for Old Horses on Richmond Hill, on the outskirts of Douglas.

⊕	Location	Douglas Promenade
🕐	Open	May–Sept. Daily from 09:00
💷	Tariff	Fares charged
🚗	Parking	Ample
♿	Disabled access	Limited Access on request
☎	Landline	+ 44 (0) 1624 696420 or 674594
🌐	Website	www.douglas.gov.im

Groudle Railway

Re-built and operated entirely by volunteers the Groudle Railway is a stunning example of what can be achieved with modest capital and endless enthusiasm. The line begins within the beautiful glen and runs for three quarters of a mile out onto the rugged Groudle headland. At its final stopping point the line overlooks the ruins of enclosures where Sea Lions and even Polar Bears were displayed for the pleasure of Victorian visitors. Trains run on Sundays between April and September, on Wednesday evenings in July, and Tuesday and Wednesday evenings in August. At Christmas locals flock to the glen to ride on the Santa and Mince Pie special trains, whilst at Easter the Bunny Express is equally popular! If railways aren't your thing, Groudle offers spectacular glen and coastal walks and a small shingle beach.

	Location	Groudle Glen Onchan
	By MER	From Douglas, Laxey and Ramsey
	Open	Sundays Apr-Sept 11:00 - 16:30 Tues - Wed Jul-Aug 19:00 - 21:00
	Tariff	Fares charged
	Parking	Ample
	Disabled access	Extremely limited access
	Landline	+ 44 (0) 1624 670453
	Website	www.groudleglenrailway.com

The Great Laxey Mine Railway

Mining for lead and zinc began in Laxey around 1780 and by the mid 1870's the Great Laxey Mine had become one of the most profitable metal mines in Britain. At the height of its success shafts were sunk to depths in excess of 2000 feet and around 1,000 men, women and young boys were employed.

The tramway wagons, originally pulled by ponies, were replaced by steam locomotives in 1877 to transport ore from the mines to the washing floors. Today a restored section of the railway, using the original locomotives 'Ant' and 'Bee,' runs for a quarter of a mile from the washing floors, under the main road and MER Railway track and up the valley towards the Laxey Wheel. Operated by volunteers the line is open 11am to 4.30pm on Saturdays and Bank Holidays from Easter until the end of September.

⊕	Location	Laxey
	By Bus	3, 3A, 3B and 3C
	By MER	From Douglas or Ramsey
	Open	Easter - Sept Saturdays and Bank Holidays
		11:00 - 16:30
£	Tariff	Fares charged
	Parking	Ample
♿	Disabled access	
☎	Landline	+ 44 (0) 1624 861706

Bus services commence from Douglas and Ramsey Bus Stations.
See pages 185 and 186

Orchid Line Miniature Railway

Operated by Manx Steam and Model Engineering Club volunteers the railway is located at the Curraghs Wildlife Park in Ballaugh, in the north of the Island. Opened in 1992 the railway was originally 550 feet long but was later extended, first to 1750 feet then to just over 3000 feet in 2000. Trains run from the station through the Ark section, over a roadway and bridge to a wooded swamp area, through a tunnel on to the children's farm then make their way back to the station. Trains run, weather permitting, most Sundays and bank holidays. The railway gets its name from the wild orchids that grow in the area.

⊕	Location	Sulby
🚌	By Bus	5, 5A and 6
🎫	Open	12:00 - 16:30
💷	Tariff	Fares charged
🚗	Parking	Ample
♿	Disabled access	Wheelchair loan service available from the Curraghs Wildlife Park
☎	Landline	+ 44 (0) 1624 897323
🌐	Website	www.mers.org.im

Bus services commence from Douglas, Ramsey and Peel Bus Stations
See pages 185 and 186

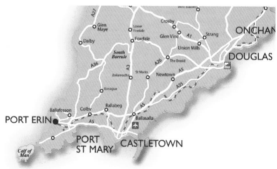

The Port Erin Railway Museum

A magnet for steam train enthusiasts the museum is located within the parameters of the Port Erin station – the line's southernmost point. Inside the museum (a former train shed) are fully refurbished steam trains, original carriages and equipment, all combining to provide an insight into the history of steam in the Island. A section of the building still performs a role as a maintenance facility for the current fleet of operational rolling stock and visitors can view the working blacksmith's workshop. The station and museum are located in the heart of Port Erin and are close to all the town's amenities. A popular café is situated within the station complex..

⊕	Location	Port Erin
🚂	By IMR	From Douglas
🔲	Open	April - Nov: Daily, 10am - 5pm
💷	Tariff	Admission charge
🚗	Parking	Ample, close by
♿	Disabled access	Access
☎	Landline	+ 44 (0) 1624 836855
🖳	Website	www.visitisleofman.com

Bus services commence from Douglas and Peel Bus Stations.
See pages 185 and 186

Coast

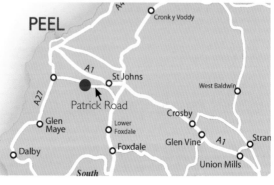

Adventurous Experiences

Adventurous Experiences is an Outdoor Education Provider, specialising in the field of Sea Kayaking and offers tailor made courses to suit individual or larger groups. Visit secret places only accessible by small craft, gaze at the spectacular sea cliffs and observe the seals, porpoises and wildlife. Also keep an eye out for Basking Sharks feeding en route! As well as Kayaking, Adventurous Experiences offer Kayak Fishing, Coasteering, Triton rides and Corporate sessions. One to One tuition is also available.

Coasteering

The Isle of Man is an ideal location for those seeking the adrenalin rush coasteering provides. Experienced thrill-seekers and even families are kitted up in a wetsuit, buoyancy aid and helmet before being led by an experienced instructor along a route that hugs the Island's rocky coastline. When the rocks become an obstacle, participants take to the water and swim to the next section!

⊕	Location	Adventurous Experiences 'The Shack' Ballabrooie, Patrick Road, St Johns
🚌	By Bus	7A
📱	Mobile	+ 44 (0) 7624 406655
☎	Landline	+ 44 (0) 1624 843034
✉	Email	info@adventurousexperiences.com
🖱	Website	www.adventurousexperiences.com

Bus services commence from Peel Bus Station.
See pages 185 and 186

 Areas for Basking Shark sightings between Mar and Nov 2007

Basking Sharks

The basking shark (Manx name Gobbag Vooar - big mouth) is the second largest fish in the world. The Isle of Man is fortunate enough to have a large number of them from May to September and it is recognised as an international hotspot. Sightings are most common on the west and southwest coast of the Island.

Although the largest recorded basking shark was 13.7m long (longer than a bus), most people only see the fins and nose projecting above the surface. Headlands are good locations for observers. Diving birds are a good indication that sea life is abundant in an area.

Interesting Facts

1) It is not known how long basking sharks live but it may be 30-50 years.
2) Basking sharks are dark grey, almost black and light coloured scars are common.
3) Their skin was traditionally used to sole fishermens boots as it provided such a good grip on slippery surfaces.
4) They are named basking sharks because of their habit of 'basking' at the surface of the water.
5) They feed by filtering out plankton from the water in a similar manner to whales.
6) Despite their huge size they are completely harmless to man.

Basking sharks, whales, dolphins and porpoises are all protected under the Manx Wildlife Act. For fantastic images and stories of basking sharks in Manx waters visit www.manxbaskingsharkwatch.com and don't forget to log on and report any sightings you may have.

☎ Landline	Manx Wildlife Trust 01624 801985
🖱 Website	www.manxbaskingsharkwatch.com

Boat Charters

The Isle of Man offers some of the most dramatic and beautiful coastal scenery in the British Isles and what better way to experience it than from a boat. Charters are available from a range of operators and can be used for a day's whale watching, fishing, bird-watching, diving or simply cruising and taking in the views. Cameras are a must with inquisitive seals, dolphins, whales and basking sharks all commonly seen in Manx waters! When booking a boat trip, why not enquire whether the operator has undergone WiSe training? WiSe operators have agreed to abide by a special Code of Conduct for each different species

KTB	01624 832339
Gemini	01624 832761
Girl Mary	01624 861724 - 07624 493592
Scraayl	01624 834307
Manx Voyager	01624 863664
Palindrome	01624 836366 - 07624 450801
Perservere	01624 620221 - 07624 496432
Foillan Beg	01624 842731
Papillion	01624 853457 - 07624 412486
Manx Sea Quest	01624 844646 - 07624 450688
Endeavour	01624 838273 - 07624 482002
Grampus	01624 844351 - 07624 480218
Castaway	01624 822788
Seyrsnys 2	01624 833133 - 07624 493824

Raad ny Foillan
Manx Coastal Walk

Coastal footpaths

Much of the Island's extraordinary coastline can be enjoyed from the land using the extensive network of footpaths – the longest of which, Raad ny Foillan circles the Island for 95 miles. The walk, which varies in difficulty, can be tackled in sections and is clearly way-marked with a white gull on a blue background. Sturdy footwear and appropriate clothing are recommended and walkers are requested to strictly observe the country code – below….

Country Code

Please do....

Keep to paths across farmland.

Close all gates unless it is obvious that they are intended to stay open.

Keep dogs under control.

Clear up your litter, particularly glass.

Please don't....

Disturb livestock.

Drop lighted cigarette ends.

Pick wild flowers.

Disturb birds' nests.

Damage walls of fences.

Trespass on private property.

Foul pools or streams.

Damage crops.

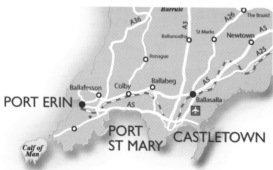

Diving

The Isle of Man is widely recognised as one of the finest areas for diving around the British Isles. Renowned for its clear water and varied underwater flora and wildlife it is growing in popularity all the time. Two Island based organisations – Discover Diving and Mann Scuba Diving – offer a range of services and equipment for both novices and experienced divers.

	Specialist	**Discover Diving,** Port St Mary
	Landline	+ 44 (0) 1624 833008
	Mobile	07624 482002
	Email	info@discoverdiving.im
	Website	www.discoverdiving.im

	Specialist	**Isle Of Man Diving Holidays**
	Landline	+ 44 (0) 1624 833133
	Email	mkeggen@manx.net
	Website	www.isleofmandivingholidays.com

	Specialist	**Mann Scuba Diving,** Port Erin
	Landline	+ 44 (0) 1624 835202
	Mobile	07624 425458
	Email	manndivers@manx.net
	Website	www.mannscubadivers.co.uk

Bus services commence from Douglas, Port Erin and Peel Bus Stations. See pages 185 and 186

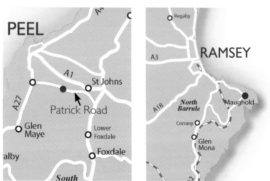

Sea Kayaking

One of the finest ways to enjoy the coast is in a sea kayak and given the Island's amazing water clarity, very often it's possible to see way down to the bottom. Discover secret coves and caverns and observe marine life close up - the unobtrusive kayak has minimal impact on its surroundings and often attracts the more inquisitive seals. Coastal kayaking trips can be arranged for anyone from eight to 80 and offers views like nowhere else in the world.

In a kayak you're at one with nature. See marine life, awe-inspiring cliffs, stunning rock formations, dart in and out of sea caves and caverns and marvel at the distorted arch-like formations.

Specialist	**Adventurous Experiences**, Patrick
Bus	7A
Mobile	+ 44 (0) 7624 406655
Landline	+ 44 (0) 1624 843034
Email	info@adventurousexperiences.com
Website	www.adventurousexperiences.com
Specialist	**The Venture Centre**, Maughold
Bus	16, MER
Landline	+ 44 (0) 1624 814240
Email	contact@adventure-centre.co.uk
Website	www.adventure-centre.co.uk

Bus services commence from Peel Bus Station.
See pages 185 and 186

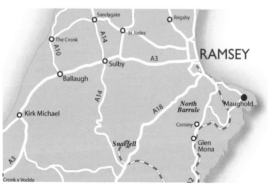

The Venture Centre,

The Island's premier outdoor activity centre was founded in 1981 and has been run since then by the Read Family. The unique location of the Centre makes it an ideal venue for a wide range of outdoor pursuits. The glen to the north side contains the Centre's purpose built assault course. Archery and Orienteering take place on fields next to the Centre.

Canoeing, sailing, kayaking, gorge walking, abseiling, climbing, raft building and archery are just some of the adventure activities on offer to children and adults.

⊕	Location	Lewaigue Farm, Maughold
	By Bus	16. MER
	Open	February - November
£	Tariff	Contact for prices
	Parking	Ample
☎	Landline	+ 44 (0) 1624 814240
✉	Email	contact@adventure-centre.co.uk
	Website	www.adventure-centre.co.uk

Bus services commence from Ramsey Bus Station.
See pages 185 and 186

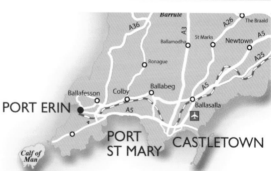

7th Wave

Situated in Port Erin 7th Wave is the only dedicated, commercial watersports facility in the Isle of Man. It is an RYA Recognised Training Centre providing dinghy sailing, powerboat and shorebased courses. They offer an action packed childrens programme during the school holidays, plus corporate team building days and water activities for groups and parties. 7th Wave also has kayaks available for hire from Port Erin beach and provide boat charters. Safety boats with qualified drivers are on the water throughout the season. The shop is well stocked with equipment for hire, wetsuits, buoyancy aids, beach toys, waterproof bags - everything you need for the beach or water.

	Location	Port Erin
	By Bus	1, 2, 2A, X2, 8 and IMR
	Open	Activities run from Easter to the end of October. The shop remains open till Christmas.
	Landline	+ 44 (0) 1624 836366
	Mobile	+ 44 (0) 7624 450801
	Website	www.7thwave-iom.com

Bus services commence from Douglas and Peel Bus Stations. See pages 185 and 186

Areas of sightings for Risso's, Bottlenose, Common Dolphins and Harbour Porpoise between 2007/2008

Areas of sightings for Minke Whale and Killer Whale sightings between 2007/2008

Whales and Dolphins

Combine the amazing number of species of whales and dolphins in Manx waters and the ability to watch them from the shore and you have a unique experience.

Think of the Island as an elevated viewing platform set amid the Irish Sea. Pick a calm day, have a pair of binoculars handy and sit back and savour the beauty, tranquillity and some of the most fabulous whales, dolphins and sharks you will ever see.

12 species of whales and dolphins have been recorded around Mann in recent years; regular species include Common, Risso's and Bottlenose dolphins, Porpoises, Orcas, Minke and even occasional Fin and Sei whales. Then there are basking sharks, here for courtship and pupping or the strange Sunfish and even the rare Leatherback turtle, another summer visitor.

Seals, mostly Atlantic Greys, are permanent residents and best seen hauled out at Kitterland, the islet in the Sound, between the Calf and mainland. The ferry-boat to the Calf will usually give you a close-up tour of the seals as it returns to Port Erin.

Porpoises, too, are resident throughout the year with a population around 800. They are usually seen in small groups, often feeding close to shore; favourite places include the Calf, Port St Mary, the Ayres, Laxey and Niarbyl.

To help you see all the fabulous animals check the two local websites for the 'Recent Sightings' and then go to the same place at the same time – it usually works. Typically, late spring, summer and autumn are the best times, when the sea is calmest and most species are present. See overleaf for more details.

For whales and dolphins go to:-
www.mwdw.net - cetaceans here all year.
For basking sharks go to:-
www.manxbaskingshark.com - late May to August.

January to April

Bottlenose dolphins tend to be winter visitors and groups of up to 40 get sighted along the west and south coast, from the Ayres to Port St Mary. Occasionally Humpbacks too come close to shore and sometimes Orcas are seen breaching at Niarbyl, Langness and the Ayres.

Risso's dolphins seem to be here most months but early in the year Douglas Head and south along Marine Drive to Little Ness is the best place to see them. Here you might also spot an early Minke whale while being entertained by the aerobatic choughs dancing on the up-draught with cries of 'Cheeoww'.

May to September

20th May to the end of August is basking shark season and the west is best for all the action. From the Sound northwards to Niarbyl, to Peel Castle and onwards to the Ayres, the coastal footpath provides the ideal elevated vantage point to see these amazing monsters swimming just yards from the shore.

Baskers can be really big - 'The Big Grey' was over 11 metres long with an estimated mass of 12 tonnes – about three African elephants-worth. Floating in a boat on a flat, calm sea you can find sharks just feet from you – scary and surreal, exhilarating and serene as they swirl across the surface, feeding, mouths wide agape.

Now the arrival of the herring and other shoaling fish bring the big baleen whales very close to the shore, in fact Minkes will feed and swim right up to the cliff face.

For Minke whales and basking sharks, early mornings and evenings are usually best – six to nine. It is said that the herring 'rise at seven', and from Niarbyl it is common to see Minkes and even sometimes the huge, 60 tonne Fin Whales, surface feeding on herring close to shore.

June, July and August are peak months to see Minkes feeding at the surface. On those wonderful, hot, still, summer afternoons you can sometimes watch a dozen or more Minkes from Niarbyl as they lunge feed amidst showers of diving gannets.

Our fabulous Risso's dolphins, often with young calves, are regularly to be seen close to the shore from Douglas to the Calf. An early morning favourite place is the outer breakwater at Port St Mary which provides a grandstand view – say 8.30 or 9am. Alternatively, try Langness in the evening, from Fort Island to the Herring Tower and enjoy the magic of the setting sun and watch the Risso's cavort and feed close by.

Summer brings the smaller Common dolphins and if you are in a boat you might be lucky enough to find them riding on your bow wave as they hunt around the shore.

September to Christmas

About September 12th, the herring move from the west coast and go to spawn off the east of Mann and the whales follow them.

The spawning begins near Port Soderick and as the season progresses the whales move slowly up the east coast past Douglas Head following wave after wave of spawning herring and shoals of small sprats.

By October and November the Minkes have moved north into Laxey, Bulgham and Dhoon bays where they will stay until almost Christmas.

The arrival of the squid in November sees an increase in Risso's dolphin activity along the south of the Island, but worsening weather and winter storms soon make sightings difficult as the old season passes and the new is about to begin.

Culture

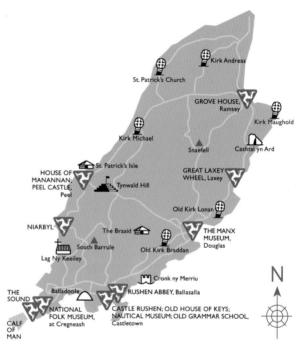

Kirk Andreas

St. Patrick's Church

GROVE HOUSE, Ramsey

Kirk Maughold

Kirk Michael

Snaefell

Cashtal yn Ard

St. Patrick's Isle

HOUSE OF MANANNAN; PEEL CASTLE, Peel

GREAT LAXEY WHEEL, Laxey

Tynwald Hill

Old Kirk Lonan

NIARBYL

The Braaid

THE MANX MUSEUM, Douglas

South Barrule

Old Kirk Braddan

Lag Ny Keeiley

Cronk ny Merriu

THE SOUND

Balladoole

RUSHEN ABBEY, Ballasalla

CALF OF MAN

NATIONAL FOLK MUSEUM, at Cregneash

CASTLE RUSHEN; OLD HOUSE OF KEYS; NAUTICAL MUSEUM; OLD GRAMMAR SCHOOL, Castletown

N

Ancient sites and burial grounds

With a heritage as rich and diverse as the Isle of Man's it's not surprising to discover that the Island is a treasure trove of sites of archaeological significance. Ancient sites and burial grounds have been discovered all over the Island and are carefully monitored and preserved. There are around 141 listed ancient monuments under the care of Manx National Heritage. The parish of Maughold in the north-east of the Island, produced the largest collection of crosses and slabs during the early Christian period (6th-13th century). Most were found in the churchyard, which was once the site of a Celtic Monastery. The elaborately carved crosses can be seen in the grounds of the current church, parts of which date back to 1000 AD. The map opposite shows the wide-ranging distribution of the main historical sites, which form part of Manx National Heritage's award winning 'Story of Mann.'

 National Heritage Museum Sites

 Early Christian Sites with Stone Crosses

 Early Domestic Sites

 Early Christian Sites

 Prehistoric Sites

 Promontory Forts

 Viking Burials

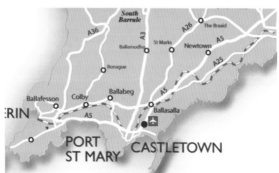

Manx Aviation and Military Museum

The museum, which opened in 2000, welcomes visitors at weekends, bank holidays and throughout the two weeks of the TT Festival. The museum is dedicated to the memory of those who served the military on the Island and who went to serve in the UK and overseas. In particular it commemorates those who lost their lives in over 200 flying accidents in and around the Isle of Man, or while serving overseas. The museum lies within the parameters of Ronaldsway Airport in the south of the Island.

⊕	Location	Ronaldsway Airport
🚌	By Bus	1,1C, 2, 2A, 8
🗐	Open	Open Weekends, Bank Holidays and TT fortnight 10.00 am to 4.30 pm.
£	Tariff	Free
☎	Landline	+ 44 (0) 1624 829294
✉	Email	webmaster.maps@iofm.net
♛	Website	www.maps.iofm.net

Bus services commence from Douglas, Port Erin and Peel Bus Stations. See pages 185 and 186

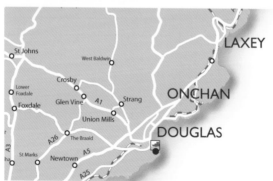

Great Union Camera Obscura

The first camera on this site was opened in 1887, but burned down within the same year. The present Great Union Camera Obscura located on Douglas Head was opened in the 1890s and is one of only a few open in the British Isles. Owned by the Heaton family from 1907 until the 1990s, the site fell into disrepair before it was acquired by the Isle of Man Government. The camera was a popular novelty in its day and used primarily to spy on other tourists cuddling on the headland! Now fully restored it's proving equally popular with modern day visitors.

Location	Douglas Head
Open	May till end of Summer. Weather permitting. A flag flies when it's open. Saturday, 1pm - 4pm Sunday, 11am - 4pm Easter Weekend Saturday - Monday, 11am - 4pm
Tariff	Admission charged Accompanied children - free
Disabled Access	Limited by doorway width and lighting
Website	www.iomguide.com

The Gaiety Theatre

The Gaiety is one of the finest examples in the British Isles of the work of Victorian theatre architect Frank Matcham. First opened in 1900 the theatre was the subject of a 10-year restoration project completed in 2000 and work continues to maintain its Victorian splendour. Contact the box office for details of tours.

The theatre is next to the Villa Marina on Douglas promenade. The two venues present a year-round programme of film, art, music and theatre.

The Gaiety Theatre is home to the only surviving 'Corsican trap' or 'ghost glide' in the British Isles, possibly the world. The specialised trap was devised to make an actor or 'ghost' appear through the stage and glide and rise across the stage. Indeed, the theatre is reputed to be haunted by several ghostly presences.

⊕	Location	Douglas Promenade
🚌	By Bus	3, 3A, 3B, 3C, 24, 26 and 28
🎫	Tickets from	Welcome Centre Sea Terminal Monday to Saturday 9.30 am to 6pm Sunday 10.00am to 2pm
♿	Disabled access	Access and toilets
☎	Box Office	+ 44 (0) 1624 694555
🖱	Website	www.villagaiety.com

Bus services commence from Douglas, Ramsey Port Erin and Peel Bus Stations. See pages 185 and 186

Ghost Walks

Come and take a walk on the dark side of Island life through the twisting back streets and lanes of Douglas, Peel, Ramsey and Castletown. With the aid of our local guides you will visit eerie castles, haunted streets and visit places of execution and public humiliation. Hear about the last Manx witch to be burnt at the stake, the White Lady of Castle Rushen and the famous Black Dog of Peel Castle, places of murder, ghostly apparitions and strange goings on. All walks continue regardless of weather - in fact, the darker, foggier and murkier the better! Come along if you dare.

⊕	Location	See website for tour details
£	Tariff	From £4 per person
♿	Disabled access	Please phone for details.
📱	Mobile	+44 (0) 7624 466094 or 416824
🖱	Website	www.iomghosttours.com

Laxey Heritage Trust

Laxey Heritage Trust is operated by a group of volunteers who live in and around the village. The Trust promotes and presents aspects of the village's chequered history as a mining village and tourist area. An Information Centre run by the Trust is located on Mine's Road and visitors can learn more about the area and its attractions. Manx crafts and gifts are available for purchase. .

⊕	Location	Laxey
	By Bus	3, 3A, 3B, 3C, 13, MER
	Open	Easter, then mid May - September
£	Tariff	Free for certain attractions
	Parking	Ample
♿	Disabled Access	Limited Access
☎	Landline	+ 44 (0) 1624 862007
	Website	www.visitisleofman.com

Bus services commence from Douglas and Ramsey Bus Stations. See pages 185 and 186

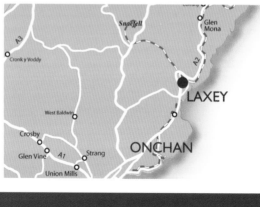

Laxey Woollen Mills

The Mill was founded by John Ruskin in 1881 and the original loom remains operational to this day. Laxey Woollen Mills produces a range of unique Manx tartans and offers for sale a wide selection of goods ranging from hats, scarves and kilt skirts to capes, rugs and giftware. The cloth for Manx tartan is produced from local wool. Also produce wool and woven cloth from Manx Loaghtan sheep, a hardy breed, native to the Isle of Man and currently enjoying a revival due to the high quality, low fat content of their meat.

	Location	Laxey
	By Bus	3, 3A, 3B, 3C,13, MER
	Open	All Year: Monday - Saturday, 10am - 5pm
	Tariff	Free
	Parking	Ample, close by in Car Park
	Disabled access	Limited access
	Landline	+44 (0)1624 861395
	Website	www.visitisleofman.com

Bus services commence from Douglas and Ramsey Bus Stations. See pages 185 and 186

Barry Edwards

Manx Transport Museum

This is an Aladdin's Cave of transport memorabilia both past and present. Housed within a restored building in Peel are many models, photographs and unique exhibits which catalogue the many different and sometimes obscure, means of transport adopted by Manx residents over the decades. It's a place full of nostalgia and surprises.

⊕	Location	Peel
🚌	By Bus	4, 4B, 5, 5A, 6, 6A, 8
🕮	Open	Easter to end of September Saturdays 11am - 4.30pm Sundays/Bank Holidays 1pm - 4.30pm
♿	Disabled Access	Step at entrance - narrow walkways
💷	Tariff	Free
🚗	Parking	Ample
☎	Landline	+44 (0)1624 842448
♿	Website	www.visitisleofman.com

Bus services commence from Douglas, Ramsey and Port Erin Bus Stations. See pages 185 and 186

Tynwald

The Manx Parliament, Tynwald has been around for over 1,000 years and is the world's oldest continuous parliament. The Branches of Tynwald, the Legislative Council and the House of Keys, sit in their separate chambers in Douglas to consider Bills. Bills which are passed by both Branches and then signed by a majority of each Branch when sitting together in Tynwald and which receive Her Majesty's Royal Assent, become law in the Isle of Man.

When the Branches sit together in the Tynwald Chamber in Douglas, they form the Tynwald Court. Tynwald Court authorises the expenditure of the Isle of Man Government and scrutinises its administration.

Members of the public are welcome to view the proceedings from the Public Gallery. Order Papers for the sitting in progress are available from the Messengers in the Lobby..

⊕	Location	Douglas
	Open	Guided tours by arrangement Mon-Fri during normal working hours
£	Tariff	Free
🚗	Parking	Car parks near by
♿	Disabled Access	Access
☎	Landline	+44 (0) 1624 685500
🖱	Website	www.tynwald.org.im

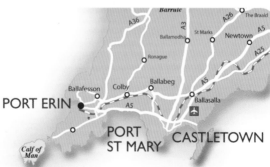

Erin Arts Centre

It is not difficult to realise why, since its opening in 1971, the Erin Arts Centre has established itself as an important venue in the Isle of Man. Community-based, it provides an essential and unique access to, and participation in, arts- based activities. It is the only locally accessible arts venue with appropriate facilities – a dedicated performance space and exhibition gallery space with full access for the disabled – for the presentation of arts, whereby performance, participation and enjoyment can be encouraged and advanced. Home to the Mananan and Opera Festivals, the Centre presents internationally renowned artists each year. It is also the venue for the Barbirolli International Oboe Festival and Competition as well as the Lionel Tertis International Viola Festival and Competition, held triennially. Recently the Centre has attracted film enthusiasts to the showing of both World Wide productions and films made on the Isle of Man. The fine acoustics of the Isle of Man Bank Auditorium is suitable for nearly all forms of art.

⊕	Location	Port Erin, Victoria Square
	Open	All Year
	Tariff	Admission Charged
	Parking	Limited - car park nearby
♿	Disabled Access	Access
☎	Box Office	+44 (0) 1624 832662
✉	Email	information@erinartscentre.com
	Website	www.erinartscentre.com

Bus services commence from Douglas Bus Station.
See pages 185 and 186

Food and Farming

The Isle of Man owes its beautiful, countryside to manx farming. Quality produce can be found in many restaurants, markets, shops, supermarkets and farms throughout the island. Taste the flavours, and take them home!

Find out about farmers markets, recipes and more on www.ilovemanx.org/index.html

Alexander Nurseries
Alexander Drive, Douglas, 675829 (Vegetables, Herbs, Plants)

Ballakilley Farm
Church Road, Port St Mary, 836626 (Vegetables, Fruit, Honey)

Brown Cow Bakery
Booa Dhone, Main Road, Santon, 829459 (Bread, Cakes, Biscuits, Desserts)

Bry Rad Fresh Manx Produce
Rye Hill, St Judes, 880422 (Vegetables, Fruit)

Cronaback Farm Shop
Bradda Road, Port Erin, 834197 (Preserves, cut flowers, plants vegetables fruit)

Davison's Ice Cream
Mill Road, Peel, 844111 (Ice Cream)

The Farmer's Den
Pooil Vaaish Farm, Arbory, 822992 (Vegetables, Preserves, Cakes, Bread, Eggs, Plants, Crafts)

Greeba Farm Ltd
Main Road, Crosby, 851611 (Mushrooms)

The Good Loaf
45 Selbourne Drive, Douglas, 617927 (Bread, Cakes)

IoM Beekeepers Association
Anchorage, Athol Park, 832355 (Honey, Candles, Wax)

Island Sheepskin Rugs
Tanyard House, Ballahowin, 851843 (Sheepskin Rugs)

Lady B Homebake
18 Alexander Drive, Douglas, 616510 (Bread, Biscuits, Cakes)

Linda's Homemade Preserves
The Hibernian, Maughold, 816157 (Preserves)

Purely Plants
Ballacannell, The Dhoor, 813358 (Vegetables, Herbs, Plants)

Radcliffe Butchers
4-6 Malew Street, Castletown, 822271 (Organic meat)

Staarvey Farm Herbs
Staarvey Farm, Staarvey Road, 801387 (Herbs)

T & P Kermeen Butchers
Main Road, Onchan, 676593 (Manx meat, Loaghtan lamb)

W A Moore
Balladoole Farm, Castletown, 822270 (Organic veg.)

The One Stop Shop
Ballaugh Bridge, 897 222 (Licensed game dealer and veg producer)

Pure Produce members

Isle of Man Meat
Website: http://www.isleofmanmeat.com
E-mail: enquiries@isleofmanmeat.com

Isle of Man Creameries
Website: http://www.isleofmancreameries.com
E-mail: enquiries@iomcreameries.com

Moore's Kippers, Moore's Traditional Curers
5-6 Mill Road, Peel, 843622 (Kippers, Shellfish, Smoked Salmon, Smoked Bacon) www.manxkippers.com

Jimbo's Manx ice cream www.manxicecream.com

Manx Spirit www.manx-spirit.com

Bushy's Beer www.bushys.com

Island Seafare, Port St Mary, 834494 www.islandseafare.co.uk

Manx Loaghtan www.manxloaghtan.com

Supermarkets Shoprite, Manx Co-operative, Tesco, & Spar also supply a range of Manx food.

Manx Museum National Library and Archives

For over a century manuscripts, plans, maps, photographs, films and printed works have been actively collected and preserved on behalf of the Manx nation. Housed within the highest level of modern archival storage, these now form a rich central resource of information on all aspects of Manx heritage, history, landholding, law, folklore, government, international trade and relations, language and genealogy.

The public reading room is open 'free-of-charge' to Island residents and visitors and every year many thousands of people make use of it for their research.

The library is open from 10am to 5pm Monday to Saturday inclusive and has information on all aspects of the Isle of Man.

It is essential that teachers make a preliminary visit before bringing a group of pupils to the library. This gives the library staff an opportunity to discuss how pupils can use the facilities most effectively, and come prepared for their research e.g. preliminary reading lists etc. The reading rooms in the library are for quiet study only. Four to five pupils maximum can be accommodated at any one time. Visits to the library are by prior arrangement, as this gives staff the opportunity of preparing materials and information for pupils and advising of times when staff and space are available.

Libraries

There are quite a few public libraries on the Isle of Man. Most libraries are operated by the local commissioners and located in more populated areas of the island. People from outside the library's local area may be required to pay a small membership charge, but this is normally only necessary if they wish to borrow items

Henry Bloom Noble Library
10/12 Victoria Street Douglas Tel: +44 (0) 1624 696461

Onchan Public Library
Willow House Main Road Onchan +44 (0) 1624 621228

Ramsey Library
Parliament Square Ramsey IM8 1RT +44 (0) 1624 810146

Ward Library
38 Castle Street Peel +44 (0) 1624 843533

Castletown Civic Centre and Library
Farrants Way Castletown +44 (0) 1624 825005

Family Library (formally Junior Library)
Nobles Hall Westmoreland Road Douglas +44 (0) 1624 671043

George Herdman Library,
Orchard Walk, Bridson Street, Port Erin. +44 (0) 1624 832365

Small annual charge to join but FREE to all VISITORS plus FREE ACCESS to the internet.

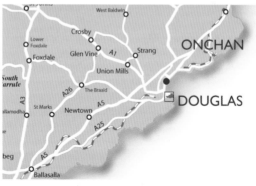

Villa Marina

The Isle of Man's entertainment history reached a milestone in 2004 with the opening of the re-vamped Villa Marina. The venue provides first-class facilities for conferences, meetings, exhibitions and functions.

The Department of Tourism and Leisure's Villa Marina provides a worthy sister venue to the Gaiety Theatre. Presenting an exciting year-round programme of entertainment, theatre, film, art and music for all, both venues pride themselves on a warm welcome to both Islanders and visitors alike.

⊕	Location	Douglas Promenade
	By Bus	3, 3A, 3C, 24, 26 and 28
	Open	All Year
£	Tariff	Varies
	Parking	Chester St. Car Park (free after 7pm)
♿	Disabled Access	Access. Toilets. Please advise when booking seats if a wheelchair position is required
☎	Landline	+44 (0)1624 694555
	Website	www.villagaiety.com

Bus services commence from Douglas Bus Station.
See pages 185 and 186

Story of Mann

Introduction

The Story of Mann is the main public presentation of the award winning work of Manx National Heritage.

It is a unique portrayal by MNH of cultural and heritage assets across 227 square miles (588 square kilometres) of historic and scenic landscape.

The Story of Mann concept preserves, presents and promotes a combination of historic properties, ancient monuments, natural landscapes and formal museums, by emphasising the interlinked nature of these assets in the historic story of the Island's development.

The Story begins at The Island's Treasure-House ('Thie Tashtee Vannin' in Manx), otherwise known as The Manx Museum - headquarters of Manx National Heritage in the Island's capital, Douglas. Here, award-winning museum displays and the latest video technology introduce 10,000 years of Manx history and invite you to explore the rest of the Island's rich heritage.

Castle Rushen

A building of huge historical significance Castle Rushen is one of the best preserved medieval castles in Europe. The Castle is situated at the centre of Mann's ancient capital, Castletown. Its origins can be found in the Norse period when Norse Kings fortified a strategic site guarding the entrance to the Silverburn River. The Castle was developed by successive rulers of Mann between the 13th and 16th centuries and its towering limestone walls would have been visible over much of the south - a continual reminder to the local population of the dominance of the Kings and Lords of Mann. Interactive displays throughout the castle include the skillfully replicated sights, sounds and smells of the past.

	Location	Castletown
	By Bus/Rail	1, 1C, 2, 2A, 8, IMR
	Open	Easter to October, Daily from 10am - 5pm
	Tariff	Admission charged
	Parking	Nearby
	Disabled Access	Limited
	Landline	+44 (0) 1624 648000
	Email	enquiries@mnh.gov.im
	Website	www.storyofmann.com

Bus services commence from Douglas, Port Erin and Peel Bus Stations. See pages 185 and 186

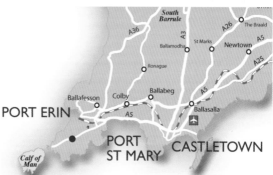

The National Folk Museum at Cregneash

Cregneash is a prime example of how the island's heritage is far from frozen in time. The village is a living museum showing what life was like in a 19th century Manx crofting community. Its isolated position ensured the village kept its unique traditions and skills into the early 20th century. In 1938 the first building was opened to the public - Harry Kelly's cottage. Kelly was a Manx crofter and Manx Gaelic speaker. The village houses a collection of thatched white-washed cottages and a working farm where, at certain times of the year, there are demonstrations of horse drawn farming techniques, blacksmithing, joinery, wool dying, spinning, weaving and traditional Manx cooking. Situated in the heart of Cregneash is the Village Tea Rooms, which offers a delightful menu including afternoon teas, scones & traditional Manx bonag.

⊕	Location	Cregneash
🚌	By Bus	1
🗐	Open	Easter to Oct: Daily, 10am - 5pm
💷	Tariff	Admission charged
🚗	Parking	Ample close by
♿	Disabled Access	Limited
☎	Landline	+44 (0) 1624 648000
✉	Email	enquiries@mnh.gov.im
♛	Website	www.storyofmann.com

Bus services commence from Douglas and Port Erin Bus Stations. See pages 185 and 186

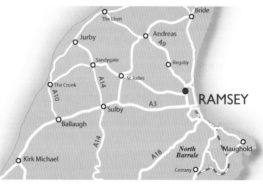

The Grove Museum of Victorian Life

The Grove, on the outskirts of Ramsey, was once the summer retreat of 19th century Liverpool shipping magnate Duncan Gibb and his family. It has been preserved to provide an insight into domestic life in the Victorian era. The house is filled largely with original furniture and fittings, while out buildings house early agricultural equipment, including a horse-powered threshing mill. Relax in the gardens or enjoy a lunch or afternoon tea in the Grove Conservatory Restaurant.

On land adjoining The Grove are Manx Loghtan sheep, a primitive breed of mountain sheep which covered the hills of the Isle of Man in their thousands until the 18th century. Both male and female Loghtans usually have four horns, though two or six-horned sheep are not uncommon. 'Loghtan' is the Manx word for the rich, brown colour of the fleece.

⊕	Location	Ramsey
🚌	By Bus	12, 18, 18A, 20
🏠	Open	Easter to October, Daily from 10am to 5pm
💷	Tariff	Admission charged
🚗	Parking	Ample.
♿	Disabled access	Limited Access.
☎	Landline	+44 (0)1624 648000
⚓	Website	www. storyofmann.com

Bus services commence from Ramsey Bus Station.
See pages 185 and 186

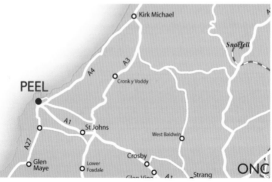

The House of Manannan

Using state of the art display techniques the House of Manannan explores the Island's Celtic, Viking and Maritime traditions. Sitting at the head of Peel Harbour, the award-winning building draws upon Manx vernacular architecture and looks across to the ancient stronghold of Peel Castle. A hugely popular attraction to visitors of all ages, the House of Manannan successfully harnesses the latest technology to bring to life aspects of the Island's heritage. There's also an excellent gift shop selling a vast array of quality souvenirs, Celtic jewellery, collectables and gift ideas.

⊕	Location	Peel
⬚	Open	Daily all year, 10am to 5pm (closed Christmas Day, Boxing Day and New Years Day)
🚌	By Bus	4, 4B, 5, 5A, 6, 6B, 8
💷	Tariff	Admission Charged
🚗	Parking	Ample
♿	Disabled access	Disabled access
☎	Landline	+44 (0)1624 648000
💻	Website	www.storyofmann.com

Bus services commence from Douglas, Ramsey and Port Erin Bus Stations. See pages 185 and 186

The Great Laxey Wheel and Mines Trail

Arguably the Island's best known landmark the Great Laxey Wheel or 'Lady Isabella' was built in 1854 to pump water from Laxey's lead and zinc mines. It is a testament to its engineering ingenuity that it's still the largest working water wheel in the world, with a diameter of 72.5ft and a circumference of 228ft. In its heyday the wheel was capable of pumping 250 gallons of water a minute from the mines 1,500 ft below ground. The mines, which once employed over 600 miners, closed in 1929 leaving the 'Lady Isabella' facing an uncertain future. The wheel and its environs was acquired by government in 1965. Today the Laxey Wheel is under the stewardship of Manx National Heritage and the wheel recently underwent a substantial refurbishment. Visitors can climb the steep spiral staircase to the viewing platform above the wheel, walk the picturesque trails and even enter a section of the mine.

⊕	Location	Laxey
	Open	Easter to October, Daily, 10am - 5pm
	By Bus/Rail	3, 3A, 3B, 3C, 13, MER
	Tariff	Admission charged
	Parking	Ample, close by in Car Park
♿	Disabled access	Limited access. Wheelchair not suitable
☎	Landline	+44 (0)1624 648000
	Website	www.storyofmann.com

Bus services commence from Douglas and Ramsey Bus Stations. See pages 185 and 186

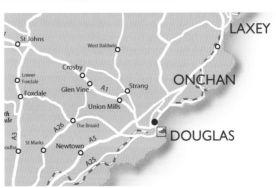

Manx Museum

The award-winning Story of Mann is introduced at the Manx Museum 'the Island's Treasure House' (Thie Tashtee Vannin), where a dramatic audio-visual film presentation invites you to discover 10,000 years of unique Manx heritage. The National Art Gallery begins the series of impressive galleries which include impressive new Viking and Medieval Galleries, extensive Social History Galleries and a fascinating new Natural History Gallery. Fine food and refreshments can also be enjoyed in the popular Bayroom Restaurant, which is situated within the Manx Museum.

	Location	Douglas
	Open	All Year Monday to Saturday 10am to 5pm. Closed Sundays, Christmas Day, Boxing Day and New Years Day
	Tariff	Free
	Parking	Manx Museum and Chester Street Car Parks
	Landline	+44 (0)1624 648000
	Disabled Access	Available
	Email	enquiries@mnh.gov.im
	Website	www.storyofmann.com

Bus services commence from Douglas, Ramsey, Port Erin and Peel Bus Stations. See pages 185 and 186

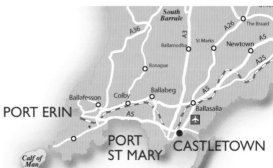

Nautical Museum

Home of George Quayle's 18th Century armed yacht 'The Peggy', this fascinating building preserves Quayle's mysterious architectural designs, and houses a replica sail maker's loft. In the fishing gallery you'll find a collection of boat models, equipment and photographs which reflect the importance of the Manx fishing industry.

	Location	Castletown
	By Bus/Rail	1, 1C, 2, 2A 8, X2, IMR
	Open	Easter to October, Daily from 10am -5pm
£	Tariff	Admission charged
	Parking	Ample close by
	Disabled access	Limited Access
	Landline	+ 44 (0) 1624 648000
	Email	enquiries@mnh.gov.im
	Website	www.storyofmann.com

Bus services commence from Douglas, Port Erin and Peel Bus Stations. See pages 185 and 186

The Niarbyl Cafe & Visitor Centre

Niarbyl is set in one of the most beautiful sections of coastline on the Isle of Man and has been renowned for generations for its spectacular views. The café and visitor centre is your starting point for exploring this historic and magnificent historic landscape. Here, high quality refreshments are available for the enjoyment of visitors, along with fascinating information on a series of special presentations about the area. Niarbyl is one of the most popular vantage points from which basking sharks, whales and dolphins can be spotted and close to the shore the area has a thriving seal population.

One of the most important geological sites in the Isle of Man is situated on the beach, where rocks from two ancient continents were forced together by movements in the earth's crust 410 million years ago.

	Location	Dalby
	By Bus	7.
	Tariff	Free
	Open	All year round
	Parking	Ample
	Disabled access	Access
	Landline	+ 44 (0) 1624 843300
	Website	www.storyofmann.com

Bus services commence from Peel Bus Station.
See pages 185 and 186

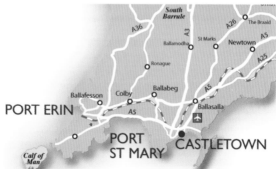

Old Grammar School

A fascinating insight into the Island's educational history, the Old Grammar School features rows of bench desks with ink wells and reminders of early Victorian school days. The former St Mary's Chapel was used as a school from around 1570. The main wing of the small, white-washed building is thought to be the oldest roofed structure in the Isle of Man – older even than all but the lowest courses of masonry of the nearby Castle Rushen. The building was saved from demolition by the trustees of the Manx Museum who, in 1950, nailed a preservation order on its door. The Manx Museum later acquired the building and carried out a sympathetic restoration project.

⊕	Location	Castletown
🚌	By Bus/Rail	1, 1C, 2, 2A, 8, IMR
🪟	Open	Easter to October, Daily from 10am to 5pm
💷	Tariff	Free
🚗	Parking	Ample, close by in car park
♿	Disabled Access	Limited
☎	Landline	+44 (0) 1624 648000
✉	Email	enquiries@mnh.gov.im
🖱	Website	www.storyofmann.com

Bus services commence from Douglas, Port Erin and Peel Bus Stations. See pages 185 and 186

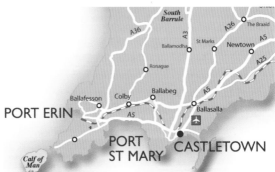

Old House of Keys

The history of 'The Old House of Keys' building, former home to the Manx Parliament, is one chapter in the long and often turbulent history of Manx politics. This is a history which stretches back to the 9th and 10th centuries when the Viking Kings ruled the Isle of Man. After it ceased to be used by Members of the Keys, the Old House of Keys building led a chequered life. Manx National Heritage took over responsibility for the building in millennium year 2000 and commenced a careful conservation programme to restore the original features of the building. The Old House of Keys has been restored to its 1866 appearance. Inside the debating chamber, visitors vote on various crucial issues which the Manx Parliament has faced in the past and some it may have to face in the future! This provides an opportunity to see how democracy developed in the Island, sometimes years ahead of England and the effect that political decisions have had and can continue to have on the Manx nation.

⊕	Location	Castletown
🚌	By Bus/Rail	1, 1C, 2, 2A, 8 IMR
🎫	Open	Easter to October, Daily. Timed admission passes are available at The Old Grammar School and Castle Rushen.
£	Tariff	Admission charged
🚗	Parking	Ample, close by
♿	Disabled Access	Limited
☎	Landline	+44 (0) 1624 648000
✉	Email	enquiries@mnh.gov.im
🖱	Website	www.storyofmann.com

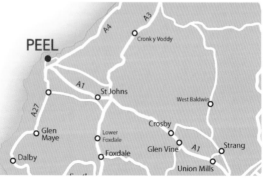

Peel Castle

Magnificent Peel Castle, one of the Isle of Man's principal historic monuments, occupies the important site of St Patrick's Isle at Peel. The Castle's Curtain Wall encircles the ruins of many buildings which are a testimony to the site's religious and secular importance in Manx history. These include St. Patrick's Church and the Round Tower from the 11th century, the 13th century Cathedral of St. German and the later apartments of the Lords of Mann. The importance of the Isle as a centre of Manx Christianity was established in the 6th century and this role was to survive the arrival of the 'pagan' Norse Vikings at the end of the 8th century. In the 11th century it became the ruling seat of the Norse Kingdom of Man and the Isles. A major six year programme of archaeological excavation commencing in 1982 emphasised the prime importance of the site. The most dramatic find was the Norse period grave of a lady of high social status; the jewellery and effects buried with her can be seen on display with other excavation finds in the Manx Museum.

⊕	Location	Peel
🚌	By Bus	4, 4B, 5, 5A, 6, 6A, 8
🕙	Open	Easter to October Daily 10am to 5pm
£	Tariff	Admission charged
🚗	Parking	Ample, close by
♿	Disabled Access	Not suitable
☎	Landline	+44 (0) 1624 648000
✉	Email	enquiries@mnh.gov.im
⚑	Website	www.storyofmann.com

Bus services commence from Douglas, Ramsey and Port Erin Bus Stations. See pages 185 and 186

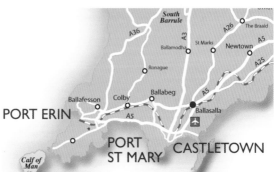

Rushen Abbey

Situated near Ballasalla are the ruins of a church built by monks. The site has been preserved by Manx National Heritage who still carry out active digs around the church. Visitors are initially welcomed into a large modern building with an interactive museum. They then pass through the museum where audio and video presentations, as well as models and signs tell the story of Rushen Abbey. Part of the museum has been specially designed for children, allowing them to be a monk, build an arch, dig for artifacts and much more. Once out of the museum visitors find themselves overlooking the ruins of Rushen Abbey. Paths and signs mark out key locations, explaining different parts of the abbey. Rushen Abbey is great for children and families with its large garden area with wild flowers, herbs and trees.

	Location	Ballasalla
	By Bus/Rail	1, 1C, 2, 8, X2, IMR
	Open	Easter to October, Daily 10am to 5pm
	Tariff	Admission charged
	Parking	Ample, close by
	Disabled Access	Access
	Landline	+44 (0) 1624 648000
	Email	enquiries@mnh.gov.im
	Website	www.storyofmann.com

Bus services commence from Douglas, Port Erin and Peel Bus Stations. See pages 185 and 186

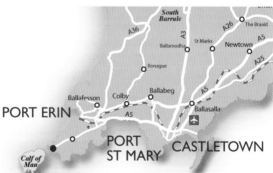

The Sound Visitor Centre and Restaurant

Located on the southern tip of the Island, the centre has panoramic glass walls and offers magnificent views of the surrounding coastline and the Calf of Man. There are information displays explaining the history and ecology of the local land and seascapes. Fine food and refreshments are available within the Restaurant and Visitor Centre. Open year round, the centre is the perfect stopping off point when taking a walk along one of the Island's many coastal paths, including the southernmost section of the Raad ny Foillan, a 95-mile long footpath that follows the coast around the Island.

There are opportunities for sighting seals or a passing dolphin off Kitterland, the rocks between the Sound and the Calf of Man.

⊕	Location	The Sound
🚌	By Bus	1.
🗔	Open	All year round
🚗	Parking	Ample
♿	Disabled access	Good
☎	Landline	+ 44 (0) 1624 838123
✉	Email	enquiries@mnh.gov.im
🖱	Website	www.storyofmann.com

Bus services commence from Douglas and Port Erin Bus Stations. See pages 185 and 186

Motorsport

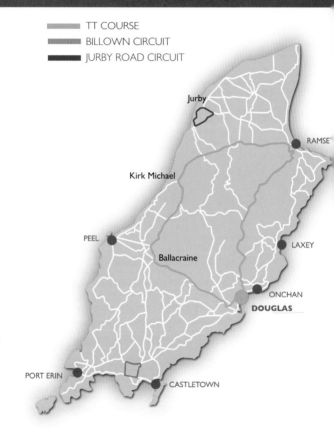

TT COURSE
BILLOWN CIRCUIT
JURBY ROAD CIRCUIT

Jurby

RAMSE

Kirk Michael

PEEL

LAXEY

Ballacraine

ONCHAN

DOUGLAS

PORT ERIN

CASTLETOWN

Motorsport Events

Andreas Racing Association - *www.andreas-racing.iofm.net*

Motorcycle road racing takes place on a regular basis between March and October each year on the newly resurfaced Jurby Airfield circuit and the adjacent 4.24-mile Jurby South public roads course providing superb trackside viewing for spectators.

Kart Racing - *www.iomkra.com*

The IoM Kart Racing Association is entering an exciting phase as it puts the finishing touches to a new 1,200 metre purpose-built track at Jurby in the north-west of the Island. Racing takes place throughout most of the year at present with a 12-round series of races for all classes.

RBS International Manx Rally - *www.manxrally.org*

The event forms round three of the prestigious Hankook MSA Gravel Rally Championship and round two of the Richard Egger Projects-sponsored MSA Asphalt Rally series.

It covers approximately 14 special stages and 120 miles of flat-out competition, timed to one-tenth of a second.

The RBS International Manx Rally has deservedly earned its place as one of the most popular events in the calendar.

Rally Isle of Man - *www.mir.co.im*

Widely acknowledged as one of the fastest road rallies in the world this event is a round of both the Tesco 99 Octane MSA British Rally Championship and the Global Group Irish Tarmac Rally Series, combining many of Britain and Ireland's leading competitors with some of the best factory built cars money can buy.

TT Races - *www.iomtt.com*

When it comes to pure road racing it doesn't come any bigger or better than the Isle of Man TT. The impetus generated by the 100th anniversary event in 2007 has launched the TT into its second century with the brightest and most exciting programme ever.

The TT is much more than a race meeting, it is a two-week festival of everything that's great about motorcycling. Supported by a myriad of bike rallies, sprints, gatherings, aerobatic and land-based displays, a packed programme of off-road action, live rock bands and the famed Manx hospitality.

International TT Rally

Event secretary: Tony East – tonyeast@manx.net

A series of vintage road runs, social gatherings and concours events over five days at the peak of the TT Festival.

Southern 100, Pre-TT Classic and Post-TT National Road Races - *www.southern100.com*

All three meetings are held on the short, but demanding 4.25-mile Billown Course on the outskirts of Castletown.

The Southern 100 was first held in 1955 over 24 laps of the course and is recognised as one of the friendliest and best organised road race meetings in the British Isles.

Manx Grand Prix *www.iommgp.com*

This event is totally amateur insofar as the riders do not receive start or prize money. This popular annual event caters for classic machines as well as modern solos and newcomers spread over a maximum of 10 races. Run on the TT Course, it is a breeding ground for riders wishing to move up to the professional ranks of the TT, but speeds are surprisingly high.

VMCC Manx Rally - *www.vmccmanxrally.co.uk*
This popular eight-day gathering includes closed road parades over sections of the TT Course on MGP race days. It features social runs, concours and timed runs.

Off-road haven
The Island has hosted world-class off-road events such as the Trial des Nations and Men's/Women's World Trials. A hectic schedule of weekly off-road trials and motocross events, is supplemented by grasstrack, enduro and beachcross. Motocross events take place at Knock Froy, Santon; West Kimmeragh, Bride; and Ballagarraghyn, Jurby, beachcross is featured at Peel, Ramsey, Douglas and Port Erin.

The Manx Two-Day Trial - *www.manx2day.com*
Is held on the middle weekend of Manx Grand Prix fortnight.

The Manx Classic Weekend Trial - *www.ManxTrials.com*
This event attracts entries from as far afield as South Africa, Italy, France, Germany and Spain.
www.isleofmanmx.com - www.manxyouthtrials.com

Busy Rally programme
The domestic rally scene in the Isle of Man has club events throughout the year. The winter months are busy with navigational rallies, now supplemented by an autocross series which has only recently been reintroduced. The Manx Rally Championship is contested over six rounds with a mixture of closed roads, forest and airfield venues, from late February to early November.
www.manxautosport.org - www.manxrc.com

MOTORSPORT

A.R.E. Motorcycle Collection

Located at the Old Vicarage in Kirk Michael this is one of the finest private collections of vintage motorcycles around. Owner Tony East opens his collection for public viewing at weekends throughout the summer. Entrance is free but donations are accepted and passed on to the Friends of the TT Riders Association. Tony's remarkable collection includes many rare and valuable machines. Manufacturers represented include Triumph, AMC, BSA, Vincent and Guzzi to name just a few.

⊕	Location	Kirk Michael
🚌	By Bus	5, 5A, 5B, 6, 6B, and 10
£	Tariff	Free (Donations TT Riders Assoc.)
🚪	Open	Weekends throughout Summer
🚗	Parking	Ample
♿	Disabled access	Limited
☎	Landline	+ 44 (0) 1624 878242

Bus services commence from Douglas, Ramsey and Peel Bus Stations. See pages 185 and 186

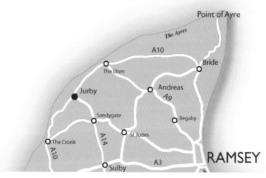

Duke Track and Kart Days

A fantastic day out at Jurby in the north of the Island for motorsport enthusiasts. Here you can check out the fast and exciting new karting facilities at Duke's newly re-designed track. Facilities include transponder timing with big-screen readout and the latest BIZ Karts all with 200cc Honda engines, geared to 35mph. Duke can cater for individuals, birthday parties, clubs, corporate and stag / hen groups. All safety equipment is provided and there's covered accommodation and refreshments on site.

The 1.5 mile Jurby Airfield circuit is used for car and motorcycle track days providing you with the chance to push your vehicle to the limit in a safe, purpose designed environment. Rules and restrictions apply.

Bikes

Location	Jurby Airfield Circuit	
Tariff	See website for tariff and details	
Open	On specific days see website	
Parking	Ample	
Landline	+ 44 (0) 1624 897121	
Website	www.duketrackdays.com	

Karts

Simply Arrive and Drive, every Sat and Sun 10:00 - 18:00hrs (Summer) or 10:00 - 16:30 (Winter) Circuit also available for private hire 7 days a week at times to suit. See website for prices.

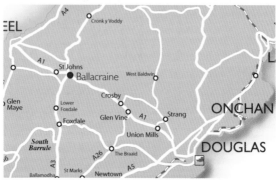

Quad Bike Trail Rides

Operated by Ballacraine Farm this is a great way to view the beautiful Manx countryside. No experience required. The quad guide will instruct and set the pace of the ride according to the capability and confidence of the riders. The emphasis is not on speed - but to enjoy the ride and spectacular views above the picturesque valley of St. Johns. The trail rises to over 1000ft with a wonderful view of the sea on each side of the Island and on a clear day a glimpse of the hills of Scotland, Wales and Ireland. Be sure to take your camera. Groups of 1 - 6 people can be accommodated on each trail, allow one and a half hours. Tea or cofffee and home-made bisuits to finish.

⊕	Location	Ballacraine
🚌	By Bus	4, 4A, 4B, 5, 5A, 5B, 6, 6B, 7A, 8 and 10
💷	Tariff	£40 per person
📅	Open	All year round
🚗	Parking	Ample
♿	Disabled access	Limited
☎	Landline	+ 44 (0) 1624 801219

Bus services commence from Douglas, Peel and Port Erin Bus Stations. See pages 185 and 186

Nature

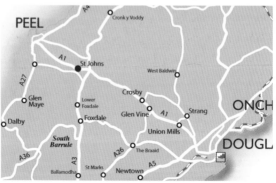

Arboretum, Tynwald National Park

Situated near Tynwald Hill, the park is also known as St Johns Arboretum. The park was created to mark the Millennium Anniversary of Tynwald (Isle of Man Parliament). The grounds were planted with trees from the 17 Manx Parishes. Wooden signs are engraved with each parish name and mark gatherings of trees, bushes and flower beds.

Paved paths wind through grass and trees, making access through the park very easy. There is also a viewing area offering access for the disabled. A variety of ducks make their home in the small lake and are always happy to receive the odd titbit. There are benches throughout the park for the comfort of visitors and children will find the enclosed playground well worth a visit.

	Location	St Johns
	By Bus	4, 4A, 5, 5A, 6, 6A, 6B, 7A, 8, 10
	Open	All Year Daily
	Tariff	Free
	Parking	Ample Car Parking
	Disabled Access	Access.
	Website	www.gov.im/daff

Bus services commence from Douglas, Ramsey, Port Erin and Peel Bus Stations. See pages 185 and 186

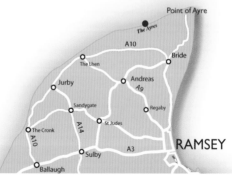

Ayres Visitor Centre

The Ayres occupy a beautiful area on the north-west corner of the northern plain. It's a nature reserve of international significance and is home to a large number of bird species and rare native flora. Bird watchers and walkers enjoy the Ayres which are made up of open areas of tundra fringed by wide, sandy beaches. Throughout the summer months the reserve is manned by a warden who leads regular guided walks in the area. The small visitor centre is well worth a visit and the notice board outside lists times and dates of significant wildlife sightings, such as the huge shoal of basking sharks that were sighted just off the shoreline in summer 2007. The marine environment surrounding the Ayres has a thriving seal population and whales are often spotted off the coast.

Visitors to the Ayres are requested to respect the delicate nature of the environment.

	Location	The Ayres
	By Bus	20 and 20A
	Open	End of May to end of September Tuesday to Sunday 1400 - 1700
	Tariff	Free
	Parking	Ample
	Disabled Access	Limited Access.
	Landline	+44 (0)1624 801985
	Website	www.gov.im/mnh

Bus services commence from Ramsey Bus Station.
See pages 185 and 186

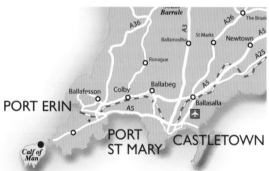

NATURE

Calf of Man

A turbulent stretch of fast moving water separates the Calf of Man from the southern tip of the Isle of Man. The Calf is a beautiful, rugged place, which is widely recognised as one of the most important bird sanctuaries in the British Isles. The Calf of Man is home to a couple of wardens throughout the summer months. Approximately 2.6km in area the Calf offers dramatic coastal scenery and complete tranquility. The large bird population includes breeding Manx Shearwaters Guillemots, Razorbills, Shags, Kittiwakes and other seabirds that can be viewed from the Calf of Man Bird Observatory. The Calf of Man is open to visitors and boat trips can be booked during the summer months. The waters around the Calf are also an important marine habitat and are popular with Scuba divers. The islet is home to a substantial seal colony and its waters are often visited by basking sharks, whales and dolphins.

There is self-catering accommodation on the Calf of Man. Enquiries and bookings should be directed to Manx National Heritage on + 44 (0) 1624 648000 or through enquiries@mnh.gov.im. Since there are no shops on the Calf of Man, visitors must bring all their own provisions.

Code of Conduct

● The Island is a sanctuary. There must be:

● No interference with the Calf's wildlife.

● No climbing equipment.

● Dogs are not allowed.

● No camping, lighting of fires, barbecues or use of naked flame stoves.

● No litter.

● No metal detecting.

● No digging.

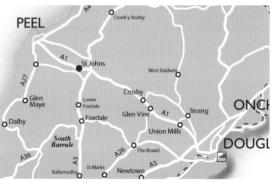

Garey ny Cloie

Situated on the A40 route between St John's village and Foxdale, Garey ny Cloie served for many years as headquarters for the Manx Forestry Department's technical operations division. Today it's a beautiful woodland garden with a huge variety of exotic tree species.

In springtime the shrub borders of evergreen azalea, dwarf rhododendron and camellia provide added colour and diversity to an already varied collection of Japanese flowering cherries which comprise early, mid-season and later-flowering varieties. The mature Japanese maple, Acer Palmatum Ozakasuki reserves its spectacular display of crimson leaf colour for the autumn.

Car parking facilities are available opposite the main gate to the grounds which are open to pedestrian visitors throughout the year. In order to maintain high standards of grounds maintenance. Dogs and cycles are not permitted.

⊕	Location	St Johns
🚌	By Bus	4, 4A, 5, 5A, 6, 6A, 6B, 7A, 8, 10
🗓	Open	All year
£	Tariff	Free
🚗	Parking	Ample
♿	Disabled Access	Limited Access. Parking
🖱	Website	www.gov.im/daff

Bus services commence from Douglas, Ramsey, Port Erin and Peel Bus Station. See pages 185 and 186

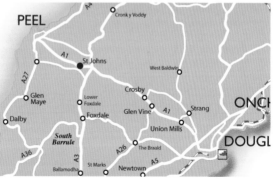

Cooil y Ree Gardens

Situated at St Johns, the Cooill y Ree gardens are a place of outstanding beauty which occupy a site of around three acres. Visitors can wander the landscaped gardens, which were officially opened by former President of Tynwald, the late Sir Charles Kerruish, in 2001. Cooil y Ree translates from the Manx Gaelic to Nook of the Kings, an appropriate name given its close proximity to Tynwald Hill, where the open air Tynwald ceremony is held every year on July 5th if it falls on a weekday or the following Monday. The gardens have been planted with a vast selection of native and non-indigenous plants and shrubs and are the perfect place to enjoy a gentle stroll on a summer's day.

⊕	Location	St Johns
🚌	By Bus	4, 4A, 5, 5A, 6, 6A, 6B, 7A, 8, 10
🚪	Open	All year
💷	Tariff	Free
🚗	Parking	Ample
♿	Disabled Access	Limited Access
🌂	Website	www.gov.im/daff

Bus services commence from Douglas, Ramsey Port Erin and Peel Bus Stations. See pages 185 and 186

Curraghs Wild Life Park

The park's natural wetland environment is a haven for endangered wildlife from around the world. There are more than 100 species of birds and animals, of which many rare species form part of international breeding programmes. Animals and birds are displayed in geographical walk-through enclosures replicating their natural habitats. Other attractions include a nature trail and butterfly trail of Manx wildlife, the Rainforest Theatre and the Orchid Line miniature railway. The park cafe offers refreshments and picnic areas in which to relax.

⊕	Location	Ballaugh
🚌	By Bus	5, 5A, 5B, 6, 6B
🗓	Open	Summer opening times, 10:00 - 18:00. Weekend opening in winter, 10:00 - 16:00
£	Tariff	Admission charge
🚗	Parking	Ample
♿	Disabled Access	Access and toilets
☎	Landline	+44 (0)1624 897323
🌐	Website	www.gov.im/wildlife/

Bus services commence from Douglas, Ramsey Port Erin and Peel Bus Stations. See pages 185 and 186

Wildlife Tourism

One of the great appeals of the Isle of Man is that without too much effort you can see a wonderful variety of wildlife. Marine life is in abundance, from colonies of nesting birds filling the air with noisy chatter to 10m long basking sharks feeding only metres from the shore. Most intriguingly of all, are the wallabies which frequent the northern plain, descendants of escapees from the Curraghs Wildlife Park. Make the most of your trip to the Isle of Man and take full advantage of the local knowledge offered by the following organisations and businesses.

Specialist	Isle of Man Wildlife Tours
Landline	+44 (0)1624 678788
Email	wildlife@manx.net
Website	www.iomtours.co.uk

Specialist	John Dog Callister
Landline	+44 (0)1624 878509
Website	www.visitisleofman.com

Home of Rest for Old Horses

The retirement home was set up in 1950 for retired tram horses. Set in 92 acres of countryside, the home is supported entirely by voluntary contributions. The Home is a registered charity (no. 620) and a member of the National Equine Welfare Council. There is an interesting museum, well stocked gift shop and home baked cooking in the Cafe. There is also a Function room for party rentals.

It's a great place to visit and is maintained by volunteer staff. The horses really enjoy visitors and always welcome an apple, carrot or a bag of feed available from the onsite shop. The location is picturesque with benches and excellent views of the surrounding countryside. Visitors will have no trouble getting a drink or snack from the cafe. Watch out for the ducks (and ducklings in summer) as well as the resident Manx cat.

⊕	Location	Richmond Hill Douglas
	By Bus	1, 1C, and 2
	Open	Mid May to Mid September Mon to Fri
	Tariff	Free
	Parking	Ample close by in car park
♿	Disabled Access	Access and Facilities
☎	Landline	+44 (0)1624 674594
	Website	www.douglashorsetramway.net

Bus services commence from Douglas and Port Erin Bus Stations. See pages 185 and 186

Mann Cat Sanctuary

A lovely place with a warm and caring atmosphere. There are many animals roaming the grounds and all are happy for attention, especially the cats. Sit and enjoy an afternoon with some very friendly felines. The sanctuary is a Manx registered charity providing a rescue and shelter service for cats in the Isle of Man. Self funding, the charity aims to rehabilitate and re-home orphaned cats and kittens and is committed to promoting responsible pet ownership, animal welfare and care. Taking care of unwanted animals is a big task which can be reduced by neutering, therefore all the cats that enter the sanctuary are neutered before being re-homed. There is a 24 hour emergency rescue vehicle available and the sanctuary is open to the public for viewings.

	Location	Santon
	By Bus	1, 1C and 2
	Open	Apr/Sept Wed/Sun Oct/Mar Sun, 2pm - 5pm
	Tariff	Free
	Parking	Ample in car park
	Disabled Access	Access
	Landline	+44 (0)1624 824195
	Website	www.manncat.com

Bus services commence from Douglas and Port Erin Bus Stations. See pages 185 and 186

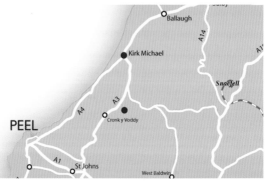

Ballahimmin Equestrian Centre

Situated amidst the beautiful Manx countryside, Ballahimmin offers trekking up into the hills. All off road trails with breathtaking scenery and an abundance of wildlife. A real family holiday experience. All standards catered for, beginners most welcome. Full instruction given by experienced, trained guides. Riding and jumping lessons. Booking necessary.

Location	Ballahimmin Farm, Off Little London Rd, Cronk y Voddy	
By Bus	10	
Tariff	Varies	
Parking	Ample in car park	
Landline	+44 (0)1624 878547	
Mobile	+44 (0)7624 482990	
Website	www.ballhimmin.com	

Pennybridge Stables

We welcome bookings for private, semi-private and class lessons (max. 6 per class). Run by qualified, enthusiastic staff. We instruct both novices and experienced riders. Range of options available from a 30 min. beginners lesson to a full pony day. Parents can drop their youngsters off for a 5hr session. Beach and country hacks available.

Location	Glebe Farm, Kirk Michael	
By Bus	5, 5A, 5B, 6, 6B,	
Open	Closed Fridays	
Tariff	Varies	
Parking	Ample in car park	
Landline	+44 (0)1624 878859	
Website	www.pennybridgestables.com	

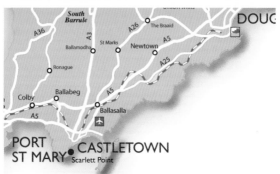

Scarlett Visitor Centre

Located in the south of the Island near Castletown, Scarlett offers a wonderful stretch of rugged coastline, perfect for walkers and bird watchers. Close to the Visitor Centre itself are some spectacular geological rock formations made up of limestone, which the forces of nature have shaped into huge pavement-like slabs. It's a place to take your camera and binoculars because the resident bird population includes an abundance of shags, cormorants, gulls, oystercatchers, ringed plover and ducks. The Visitor Centre, which opens daily between 2pm and 5pm (except Mondays) between May and September, offers a selection of books, cards and gifts for sale..

	Location	Scarlett Point, Castletown
	By Bus	1, 1C, 2, 2A and 8
	Open	May - Sept. Daily except Mon 14:00 - 17:00
	Tariff	Free
	Parking	Ample
	Disabled Access	Very limited access
	Landline	+44 (0)1624 801985
	Website	www.wildlifetrust.org.uk/manxwt/

Bus services commence from Douglas, Port Erin and Peel Bus Stations. See pages 185 and 186

National Glens

The huge number of beautiful glens which decorate the Manx landscape are a defining feature of the Isle of Man. In total there are 17 National Glens and many more smaller examples scattered around the Island. They form two distinct types – coastal and mountain, though all have their own distinctive features. The Glens are a paradise for ramblers and the perfect place to get away from it all. Sturdy footwear is recommended at all times, as most of the pathways are earth or grass. Ease of access to the glens varies and a significant number are not suitable for people with walking difficulties.

1. Elfin Glen, Ramsey
2. Lhergy Frissel, Ramsey
3. Dhoon Glen, between Laxey and Ramsey
4. Laxey Glen, Laxey
5. Silverdale Glen, nr Ballasalla
6. Colby Glen, Colby
7. Ballaglass Glen, runs to Cornaa Beach
8. Glen Maye, South of Peel towards Dalby
9. Glen Helen, St Johns
10. Glen Mooar, between Peel and Kirk Michael
11. Glen Wyllin, Kirk Michael
12. Tholt-y-Will Glen, Sulby Valley
13. Molly Quirk's Glen, Onchan
14. Port Soderick Glen, Santon
15. Groudle Glen, nr Onchan
16. The Purt, Ballaugh, Ballaugh
17. Bishops Court Glen, nr Kirk Michael

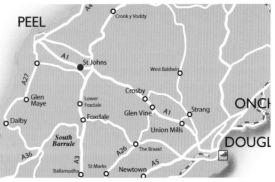

Wildflower Garden

The Manx Wildlife Trust's Wildflower Garden is the place to sit and relax, less than 100 yards from the hustle and bustle of Tynwald Mills Shopping Centre. Surround yourself with some of the most beautiful native flora in the Isle of Man. This award winning garden is cared for by the Wildflowers of Mann project team and is a showcase for wildflower gardening techniques.

⊕	Location	St Johns
	Open	All year, 09:00 - 17:00
£	Tariff	Free
	Parking	Ample
♿	Disabled Access	Accessible
☎	Landline	+44 (0)1624 801985
	Website	www.wildlifetrust.org.uk/manxwt/

Bus services commence from Douglas, Ramsey Port Erin and Peel Bus Stations. See pages 185 and 186

Leisure Activities

ANGLING

There are 4 million anglers in the UK, from those who just dangle a bit of string in the water to the dedicated all-weather enthusiast with a complete armoury of tackle.

But no matter what type of angler you are, you'll find that fishing in the Isle of Man is, quite simply, unique.

The most obvious advantage is the size of the Island. Measuring 33 miles long by 13 miles wide (approximately 50km by 20km wide) there's never far to travel to reach either a river, reservoir or stretch of quiet coastline to enjoy a day's peaceful fishing whilst savouring the tranquility of the Island. In addition, access to most rivers, reservoirs and shorelines is extremely easy.

Licences are required for fresh water fishing and are available at the DAFF offices in Rose House, Circular Road, Douglas; at the

Welcome Centre in the Sea Terminal Building and can also be purchased from most Post Offices. Several of the tackle shops on the Island also sell licences.

There are about 95 miles of coastline, ranging from sandy beaches to rocky headlands, tranquil riverbanks plus six reservoirs from which to choose. For one morning you could be fishing at high water at the rugged Point of Ayre, right at the northern most tip of the Island, then in the afternoon, you could be down in picturesque Port St Mary, at the south of the Island, fishing at low water in an area with a distinct maritime atmosphere.

Angling in the Isle of Man offers an exceptional variety of locations, from the promenade and beach in the capital, Douglas, to the peace and quiet of the reservoirs dotted throughout the Island and the idyllic settings of the rivers Dhoo, Neb, Silverburn, Santon and Sulby, some of which flow through the picturesque Manx national glens. River fishing is until the end of September, reservoir fishing until the end of October, while salmon and sea-trout fishing take place mainly in late summer and autumn.

There is an active angling fraternity on the Isle of Man, with a number of clubs happy to welcome new members. The Island also plays host to two major angling events each year when there's usually a good run of tope, and the Mannin Angling Club Angling Festival in Port St Mary. This is a large Boat fishing festival catering for both charter Boats and small Boats alike, fishing the in Shore reefs around Port St Mary and the Calf of Man. The festival also includes two Shore competitions - both from Port St Mary.

SHORE FISHING

ManxShorefishing.com - a website dedicated to fishing from the beaches, piers and rock marks of the Isle of Man. The website contains detailed descriptions of a wide variety of shore fishing marks and articles on some of the more interesting species that the Isle of Man has to offer the visiting angler, including the much sought after Tope. Also included are recent catch reports submitted by local anglers and an active forum where information can easily be obtained and exchanged.

Bowling

The Isle of Man is blessed with an abundance of bowling greens and has become a mecca for visiting crown green bowlers, both sport and recreational, since the middle of the last century. High quality greens, usually maintained by the local authorities, can be found in most of the major towns and villages of the Island (see map opposite). The Island is host to two major bowling festivals each year – normally held in June and September, at which local bowlers compete against the top bowlers from the UK.

Crown Greens are available in:
Castletown
Douglas, Nobles Park
Douglas, Finch Hill
Douglas, Villa Marina
Marown
Onchan Park
Peel
Port Erin
Port St Mary
Ramsey

GOLF COURSES

1 Castletown Golf Links +44 (0)1624 822201
Championship, 18 Holes Par 72 Men's 6711 off the Championship tees, 6534 off the medal tees. Par 73 Ladies' 5635 yards.

2 Douglas Golf Club +44 (0)1624 661558
Parkland, 18 Holes Par 69 Men's 5922 yards. Par 71 Ladies 5424.

3 Glen Truan +44 (0)1624 880359
Links 18 Hole Mens – 6651/6395 SI 71 Ladies – 5534 SI 67

4 King Edward Bay Golf Club +44 (0) 1624 672709
Links, 18 Holes Par 67 Men's 5221 yards. Par 69 Ladies' 4685 yards.

5 Mount Murray Country Club +44 (0)1624 695208
Moorland, 18 Holes Par 72 SSS 72 Men's 6664 yards off the back tees. Par 73 Ladies' 5551 yards.

6 Peel Golf Club +44 (0)1624 844232
Moorland, 18 Holes Par 69 Men's 5850 yards off the white competition tees. 5660 yards from the yellow tees. Par 72 Ladies' 5398 yards

7 Port St Mary Golf Club +44 (0)07624 497387
Hilly, 9 Holes Par 68 Men's 5702 from competition tees, (5314 yards for municipal round). Par 70 Ladies' 5274 yards.

8 Ramsey Golf Club +44 (0)1624 814736
Parkland, 18 Holes. Par 70 Men's 5960 yards. Par 72 Ladies' 5280 yards. yds.

9 Rowany Golf Club +44 (0)1624 834072
Flat, 18 Holes. Par 70 Men's 5774 yards. Par 72 Ladies' 5181 yards.

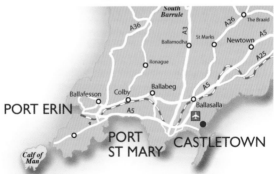

Manx Flyers Aero Club

Manx Flyers offers flight training for the PPL, NPPL and IMC ratings. They also offer trial lessons and pleasure flights for either 30 minutes or 1 hour in a 2 seater or 4 seater aircraft, with prices starting from £70 up to £160. Manx Flyers can also provide private charters through its parent company Ravenair. The clubhouse offers a wide variety of food and drink. Sunday lunch is very popular and booking is recommended, all are welcome. The clubhouse is also available for private functions.

	Location	Derbyhaven
	By Bus	1, 2, 8 connect with 2A from the Airport
	Tariff	From £70 - £160
	Parking	Ample close by in car park
	Landline	+44 (0)1624 825999
	Email	manxflyers@manx.net
	Website	www.manxflyersaeroclub.com

Bus services commence from Douglas and Port Erin Bus Stations. See pages 185 and 186

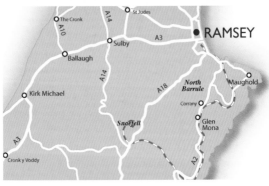

Mooragh Park

Located in the heart of Ramsey, Mooragh Park is one of the finest outdoor leisure facilities on the Island. Set within spacious manicured gardens and walkways the park offers a large boating lake, a well-equipped children's play and water area, tennis courts, bowling green, crazy golf and two excellent cafes. The larger of the two refreshment facilities is situated within a modern pavilion style building, which is often the location for a range of open-air entertainments throughout the summer months. A five-minute walk from the main town of Ramsey, Mooragh Park is the ideal place to spend a spare couple of hours or the whole day.

	Location	Ramsey
	By Bus/Rail	3, 3A, 3B, 3C, 5, 6, MER
	Tariff	Access free. Charge for some park attractions
	Parking	Ample close by
	Disabled Access	Access
	Landline	+44 (0)1624 810100
	Website	www.visitisleofman.com

Bus services commence from Douglas and Peel Bus Stations. See pages 185 and 186

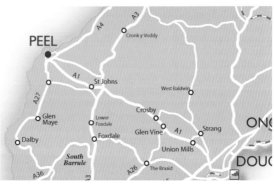

Moore's Traditional Curers

Moore's Traditional Curers is a family business and working factory, that enables visitors to experience the entire kipper making process. Take a tour of the factory and see for yourself how Manx kippers are made. Tour times can vary, especially in winter, so do call into the shop, telephone or email to check times.

⊕	Location	Peel
🚌	By Bus	4, 4B, 5, 5A, 6, 6B, 8
🗐	Open	Contact for opening times
£	Tariff	£2 Adults, £1 Children
🚗	Parking	Nearby
☎	Landline	+44 (0)1624 843622
🖱	Website	www.manxkippers.com

Bus services commence from Douglas, Ramsey and Port Erin Bus Stations. See pages 185 and 186

Mountain Biking

Where else can you scale the peaks and brush the rugged, beautiful coastline in one trail? All the beauty and diversity of the British Isles can be found on our Island, and there's plenty on offer for Mountain Bikers. Whether its competition you seek or just an opportunity to explore this amazing place, you will always find a warm Manx welcome here. Detailed maps for each route will be available from various outlets.

1 Hells 8 (15.3 mile figure of eight) This gruelling route with over 2800ft of climbing.

2 A Grand Day Out (18.6 mile loop) A long route which offers a variety of climbs and descents.

3 Witches Barrel (12.6 mile loop) This route has some tricky technical climbs and descents.

4 St Lukes to Creg Ny Baa (11.1 mile loop) Some technical climbing and flowing descents.

5 The Leg Burner (12.4 mile loop)
This loop has over 1800ft of climbing with some very technical ascents and descents.

6 Conrhenny/ Barroose (8 mile loop) A loop with a fairly technical climb.

7 Heritage Trail (10.9 miles each way) A simple trail following the old steam railway line and suitable for all the family.

8 South Barrule (2mile loop) This route is for reasonably fit cyclists capable of riding on unfinished roads with some loose surfaces.

9 Southern Comfort (13.5 mile loop) This route is for the more experienced mountain biker.

10 Camels Back (16 mile loop) For the experienced rider.

Noble's Park

A spacious and pleasant green area with views to Douglas Bay, Nobles Park offers a range of excellent leisure activities including bowling greens, children's play areas, sports fields, a skate-park and an excellent café. The park is owned and maintained to a high standard by Douglas Corporation and there is no charge for access.

Location	Douglas	
By Bus	3, 3A, 3B, 3C, 22, 23, 25	
Open	May - Sept Daily, 10am - 5pm	
Disabled Access	Access	
Parking	Ample, close by in car park	
Website	www.douglas.gov.im	

Bus services commence from Douglas, Peel and Ramsey Bus Stations. See pages 185 and 186

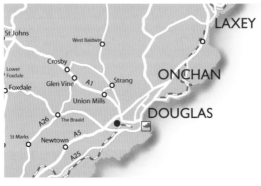

NSC

The Islands premier sport and leisure facility. The NSC boasts the following facilities:

- A competition short course swimming pool & leisure pool with 2 flumes & water features
- A full size sports hall & a 4 court secondary sports hall
- The Fitness Zone gym & spa suite
- A 5 rink indoor bowling facility
- A 6 court squash facility
- An 8 lane athletics track & field facility
- An all weather synthetic pitch
- The NSC has good access to facilities for disabled persons and also has a range of specialist equipment.

Quest

The National Sports Centre is proud to be Quest Accredited and has maintained its highly commended status since December 2001.

⊕	Location	Douglas
🚌	By Bus	1, 1C, 2, 4, 4A, 4B, 14, 21
📄	Open	See website for opening details
💷	Tariff	Separate charges for facilities
🚗	Parking	Ample in car park
☎	Landline	+44 (0)1624 688588
💻	Website	www.gov.im/sport

Bus services commence from Douglas, Port Erin and Peel Bus Stations. See pages 185 and 186

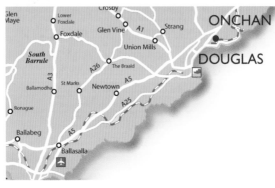

Onchan Pleasure Park

Located at the northern end of Douglas Bay within the village district of Onchan, this facility offers activities for all the family during the summer months. The stadium at the centre of the complex is the venue for regular evening stock car race meetings, but those who favour more leisurely pursuits are equally well-catered for. There's a large boating lake with motorboats for hire and bumper boats within a separate enclosure. The park also offers a putting green, bowling (flat and crown), kiddie cars, tennis courts and an exceptionally well-equipped children's play area..

	Location	Onchan
	By Bus	13, 13A, 25, 25A, 26, 26A 26B
	Open	See website for opening details
	Tariff	Separate charges for facilities
	Parking	Ample, close by
	Landline	+44 (0) 1624 675564
	Website	www.visitisleofman.com

Bus services commence from Douglas Bus Station.
See pages 185 and 186

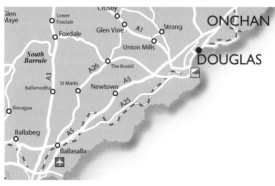

Palace Cinema

A modern two-screen facility close to the Hilton Hotel behind Douglas promenade that shows all the latest blockbusters. Well-equipped with an excellent sound system the Palace Cinema offers both a website and telephone booking system. There's ample parking outside.

⊕	Location	Central Promenade, Douglas
	Open	All year
£	Tariff	Admission charged
♿	Disabled access	No Access.
☎	Landline	+ 44 (0) 1624 627777 24 hours
🖱	Website	www.palace-cinema.com

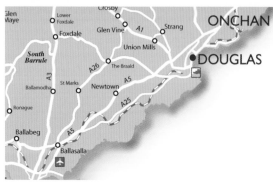

The Broadway Cinema

The Broadway Cinema in the Villa Marina on Douglas seafront, incorporates the latest cutting edge sound and projection equipment, which means you can enjoy the big-screen movie experience to the full.

The cinema presents an entertaining mix of family viewing and the latest blockbusters, with matinees for children each weekend and during school holidays as well as nightly movies.

To see which films are showing, visit the website.

The 154-seater cinema doubles as a first-class lecture theatre and is fitted with an in-built data projector.

⊕	Location	Villa Marina, Douglas Promenade
🚌	By Bus	3, 3A, 3B, 3C, 24, 26 and 28
🎟	Open	Box office open Mon - Sat 10.00 am to 4.30pm (except for public holidays). Welcome Centre Sea Terminal Mon - Sat 9.30 am to 6pm Sun 10.00am to 2pm
♿	Disabled access	Access and toilets
☎	Box Office	+ 44 (0) 1624 694555
🌐	Website	www.gov.im/villagaiety/broadway

Bus services commence from Douglas and Ramsey Bus Stations. See pages 185 and 186

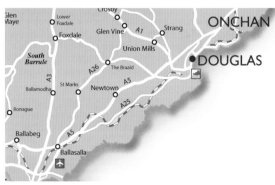

Sayle Gallery

The Sayle Gallery is located within the Villa Marina Arcade in Douglas. Named after one of the Island's finest artists, the late Norman Sayle, the gallery offers a unique opportunity to view the work of a range of talented local artists working in a variety of mediums. The gallery hosts around 18 separate exhibitions each year and attracts an estimated 26,000 visitors. An excellent selection of paintings, prints, cards and craftware can usually be purchased at the gallery..

⊕	Location	Villa Colonnade
🚌	By Bus	3, 3A, 3B, 3C, 24, 26 and 28
🗔	Open	All Year: Sat, 1pm - 5pm Sun, 2.30pm - 4.30pm Tuesday - Friday, 11.30am - 5pm
£	Tariff	Free
🚗	Parking	Ample, close by
♿	Disabled Access	Access
☎	Landline	+44 (0) 1624 674557
🖥	Website	www.thecourtyardgallery.net

Bus services commence from Douglas and Ramsey Bus Stations. See pages 185 and 186

Sporting Venues

1 National Sports Centre

Based approximately 1.5 miles from Douglas Promenade, this £20 million facility is the sporting centre of the Isle of Man. Facilities include competition swimming pool, sports halls, bowls hall, squash centre, gym and spa suite, full size synthetic pitch, 6 lane fully floodlit synthetic running track, 800 metre tarmac raceway. There is a leisure swimming pool with flume rides, flow pool, whirlpools and geysers as well as a Toddlers pool with childrens beach area and slide. Telephone +44 (0) 1624 688588

2 Castletown Swimming Pool

A heated indoor facility, maintained at 30°C, dimensions: 25m by 7.5m. There is a cafe, and excellent changing areas including facilities for disabled users. Telephone +44 (0) 1624 823930

3 Peel Swimming Pool

The 25m pool at Peel has a cafe, and excellent changing areas including facilities for disabled users.
Telephone +44 (0) 1624 842525

4 Ramsey Swimming Pool

Swimming is one of the most enjoyable, beneficial and safest forms of low impact exercise. The 20 x 10 metre pool at Ramsey offers a variety of sessions for all ages and abilities. A qualified lifeguard supervises the pool at all times. Telephone +44 (0) 1624 812852

Tennis

Noble's Park Douglas, Onchan Park, Port Erin, Mooragh Park Ramsey, Peel.

Bus and Rail Services

BUS SERVICES

For details of time schedules ask for the Free Bus and Rail timetable.
Map of routes see inside front cover
Bus services commence from Douglas, Ramsey Port Erin and Peel
Bus Stations to all towns and villages.

No I Douglas, Airport, Castletown Colby, Port Erin,
Port St Mary and Sound.

No IC Douglas, Airport and Castletown.

No 2 Douglas, Airport, Castletown, Shore Road Port Erin and
Bradda West.

No 2A Airport, Derbyhaven, Shore Road and Port Erin.

No 3 Douglas, St Ninians, Onchan, Laxey and Ramsey.

No 3A Douglas, Dukes Road, Victoria Road, Onchan, Laxey
and Ramsey.

No 3B Douglas, St Ninians, Onchan, Laxey, Ballaragh and
Ramsey.

No 3C Douglas, St Ninians, Onchan, Laxey, Old Laxey and
Ramsey. Ballaragh, Old Laxey, Laxey and Douglas

No 4 Douglas, Cooil Business Park Foxdale St Johns and Peel

No 4A Douglas, Cooil Business Park Foxdale and St Johns.

No 4B Douglas, Cooil Business Park, St Marks, Foxdale, St
Johns and Peel.

No 5 Douglas, Hospital, Crosby, St Johns, Peel, Wild Life Park.
and Ramsey.

No 5A Douglas, Crosby, St Johns, Peel and Wild Life Park.

No 5B Ramsey, Wild Life Park, Crosby, and Douglas.

No 6 Ramsey, Wild Life Park, Peel, St Johns, Hope, Crosby,
Hospital and Douglas.

No 6B Ramsey, Wild Life Park, Peel, St Johns, Hope, Crosby,
and Douglas.

No 7 Peel, Patrick Glen Maye and Dalby.

No 7A Peel, St Johns, Patrick Road and Patrick.

No 8 Peel, St Johns, Foxdale, Airport, Castletown
and Port Erin.

No 9A	Douglas, Strang, Hospital and Meadow Crescent.
No 9A	Douglas, Strang, Hospital and Meadow Crescent.
No 9B	Douglas, Strang, Hospital and Meadow Crescent.
No 9C	Douglas, Ballabrooie and Douglas.
No 10	Peel, St Johns, Glen Helen Cronk-y-Voddy and Kirk Michael.
No 11	Douglas, Strang, Hospital and Abbeylands
No 11A	Douglas, Strang, Hospital and Abbeylands.
No 12	Ramsey Town.
No 13	Douglas, Hospital, Onchan, Laxey and Old Laxey.
No 13A	Douglas, Hospital, and Onchan.
No 16	Ramsey and Maughold.
No 17	Ramsey, Jurby, Andreas, Regaby and Ramsey.
No 17A	Ramsey, Jurby, Andreas, Smeale, Bride and Ramsey.
No 18	Ramsey, Regaby, Andreas, Jurby and Ramsey.
No 18A	Ramsey, Bride, Smeale, Andreas, Jurby and Ramsey.
No 19	Ramsey, Jurby and Ramsey.
No 19A	Ramsey, Ballaugh Cronk, Jurby and Ramsey.
No 20	Ramsey, Point of Ayre, Bride, Andreas, Regaby and Ramsey
No 20A	Ramsey, Regaby, Andreas, Point of Ayre, Bride, and Ramsey
No 24A	Derby Castle and Promenades
No 25A	Douglas/Onchan Circular Service and Promenades.
No 26A	Douglas/Onchan Circular Service and Promenades.
No 27	Douglas Promenade, Onchan and Groudle
No 28	Douglas and Onchan
No 29	Douglas and Port Soderick

IMR	Steam Railway
SMR	Snaefell Mountain Railway
MER	Manx Electric Railway

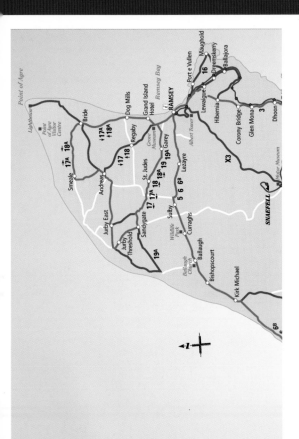

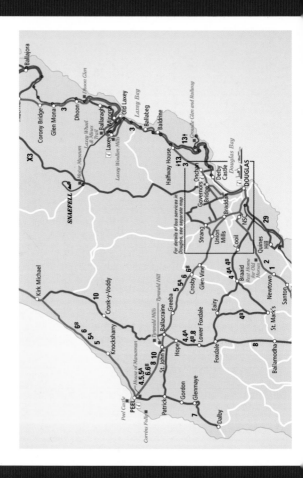

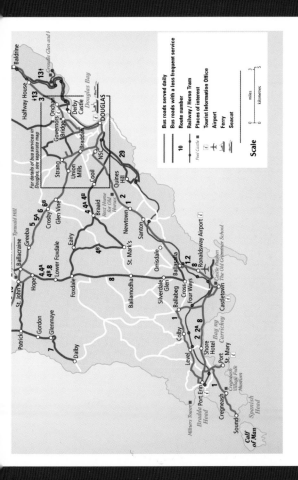

Scale

	miles	3
	kilometres	5
0		
0		

Bus roads served daily
Bus roads with a less frequent service
10   Route number
Railway / Horse Tram
Peel Castle ■   Places of interest
🛈   Tourist Information Office
✈   Airport
⚓   Ferry
      Seacat

For details of bus services in Douglas, see separate map

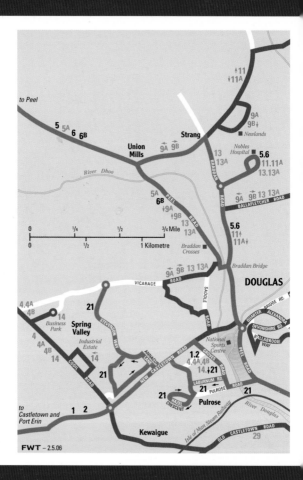

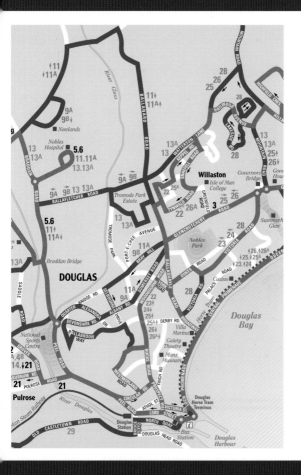

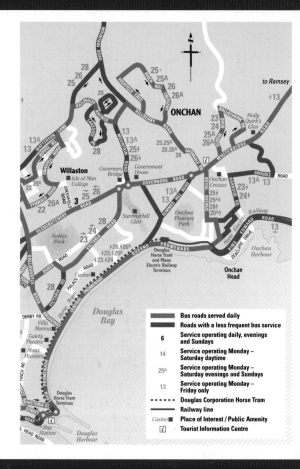

ONCHAN

Willaston

Isle of Man College

Governors Bridge

Government House

Onchan Crosses

Molly Quirk's Glen

to Ramsey

Summerhill Glen

Onchan Pleasure Park

Nobles Park

Onchan Head

Douglas Horse Tram and Manx Electric Railway Terminus

Douglas Bay

Casino

Horse Tram

Derby Rd.

Villa Marina

Gaiety Theatre

Manx Museum

Douglas Horse Tram Terminus

Victoria St.

Quay

Bus Station

Douglas Harbour

Onchan Harbour

▬▬▬	**Bus roads served daily**
▬▬▬	**Roads with a less frequent bus service**
6	**Service operating daily, evenings and Sundays**
14	**Service operating Monday – Saturday daytime**
25A	**Service operating Monday – Saturday evenings and Sundays**
13	**Service operating Monday – Friday only**
▪▪▪▪▪	**Douglas Corporation Horse Tram**
▬▬▬	**Railway line**
Casino	**Place of Interest / Public Amenity**
ℹ	**Tourist Information Centre**